CRC EXAM
GUIDE
TO
SUCCESS

NINTH EDITION

by

Roger O. Weed, Ph.D., C.R.C.

Joseph A. Hill, Ph.D., C.R.C.

CRC Exam Guide to Success
Ninth Edition
by

Roger O. Weed, Ph.D., C.R.C., C.D.M.S., L.P.C., C.C.M., F.N.R.C.A.,
Joseph A. Hill, Ph.D., C.R.C.

© 2008, Authors

ISBN # 978-0-9798786-3-3

Published by:

Elliott & Fitzpatrick, Inc.
P. O. Box 1945
Athens, Georgia 30603
706/548-8161 Inside Georgia
800/843-4977 Outside Georgia
FAX 404/546-8417

TABLE OF CONTENTS

Part	Title	Page

See following pages for expanded table of contents

PREFACE

Since beginning the CRC certification process in the mid 1970's, aspiring rehabilitation professionals have experienced anxiety over preparing for **THE** exam. Indeed, in 2007 more than 20 per cent of the examinees failed the exam. Study groups and networking have partially helped people prepare for the increasingly more valuable designation: *Certified Rehabilitation Counselor*.

Other study training guides have emerged for exam preparation but in our opinion, these guides are not focused on the exam content. Much of the information seems to be a summary of a master's degree program in rehabilitation counseling. In an effort to be more focused, students historically have been asked to comment on the CRC exam and to identify shortcomings in the university training program. This information was information passed on to other students in the form of a booklet.

Since many people preparing for the exam contacted the authors and asked for training, it became obvious that a regularly updated booklet could be valuable to others preparing for the examination. Therefore, several updated guides have been published. Each person who receives this guide is asked to offer suggestions and comments following the exam and changes are included in the next edition. We expect to continue to update the guide regularly to reflect the changing content of the exam. We hope that you, the reader, will contribute to the pool of information by giving written "feedback" to the authors. We genuinely care about each person who chooses to pursue the goal of becoming a member of an elite professional group by passing the certified rehabilitation counselor exam.

Thanks are extended for extensive original writing with hours of research for sources and documentation with previous editions by Maribeth Abrams and Joy Wilkins. Also Debbie Berens, Ann Landes, Lisa Engelhart, and Dr. Robin Dock have contributed information and comments. For this edition, Tameeka Hunter, MS, CRC tediously edited the text. Tracy Roberts, MS also offered suggestions for changes. Finally, thanks to the many test takers who provided advice and comments to previous editions of this manual.

ROW & JAH
May, 2008

INTRODUCTION

This guide assumes the reader has a formal education in rehabilitation counseling. The book contents are outlines and summaries of pertinent information. It is expected that the reader will use this guide to "synthesize" data for rapid retrieval under testing conditions.

- If topic areas seem "foreign" to you, the reader, then it is critical that additional detailed information on the subject matter be obtained. Selected references are listed at the end of the book and the CRCC offers a list of readings.

- The reader will also obtain a copy of the CRC Ethics when application is made for the examination and the document should be thoroughly reviewed before taking the exam (also available at www.crccertification.com). NOTE! The ethics document is under revision at the time that this booklet was revised.

- One of the authors, an expert in multicultural issues, observed that the reference relating to multicultural questions from the CRC Board appears not to be the correct source. The book listed is one which is very familiar to him, yet questions that candidates stated were on the exam could not be answered from information in the suggested text. As of this writing, the CRCC has not responded to our inquiry about references for multicultural questions.

- Within the past few years, the structure of the CRC exam has been changed to be more in line with the Council for Accreditation of Counseling and Related Educational Programs (CACREP). Although we have been assured that the basic pool of questions remain, the practical effects of this change is still emerging.

- Each examination also includes some field test questions that will not be used in the scoring of the examination.

- Although the Commission has a sophisticated exam item producing process, many candidates claim that questions are often poorly worded and confusing. Some who claim they are experts in some of the subject areas on the exam assert that answers are not apparent, or the wording of the question does not provide a proper foundation for answering the question. Therefore, read questions carefully.

- In Part 1, there is a list of 12 knowledge domains that CRCC uses to develop the test. Read them closely and if some areas are unfamiliar, make sure you have "filled in the blanks" before taking the test.

Information contained in this guide is presented in logical order beginning with the historical foundations of rehabilitation, including "recent" history, ethics, and diversity issues.

History is followed by vocational aspects of rehabilitation and vocational theories, which outlines relevant authors and concepts that have influenced rehabilitation.

Next is assessment in rehabilitation, which covers appropriate terms and tests.

Statistics, used to interpret testing information, is presented next. This chapter offers definitions of various terms related to reliability, validity and other important topics.

Following statistics is the medical and psychological aspects of disability chapter. A wide variety of disabilities are included. There is no separate psychological aspects section since the CRC exam does not ask many questions on this topic.

The counseling theories chapter lists a number of the more "popular" theories with terms, and other important information.

The appendices contain sample questions with answers, test taking hints, reference list and an evaluation form for this guide.

We urge all readers to send us a candid evaluation after taking the exam so we can improve this guide. Good luck!

PART 1
HISTORY AND FOUNDATIONS OF REHABILITATION

I.   Summary of Vocational Rehabilitation Laws

Laws	Emphasis	Year
Federal Employees Worker's Comp Act	Alternative to suing for work-related injuries.	1908
War-Risk Act (P.L. 65-90)	Provided rehabilitation and vocational training. Gave U.S. Government authority to insure ships at sea.	1914
Smith-Hughes Act (P.L. 64-347)	Promoted vocational education.	1917
Smith-Sears Act or Soldier's Rehabilitation Act (P.L. 65-178)	Authorized Federal Board for Vocational Education to organize and offer programs of vocational rehabilitation for veterans with disabilities.	1918
Smith-Fess Act (P.L. 66-236)	Counseling, training, prosthetic appliance and job placement to people with disabilities from industrial injuries.	1920
Vocational Rehabilitation Program (P.L. 74-271)	Became permanent part of Social Security Act.	1935
Randolph-Sheppard Act	Priority for persons who are blind in the location and operation of vending facilities on federal property.	1936
Wagner-O'Day Act	Federal government will purchase items produced in Rehabilitation Workshops.	1938
Borden-LaFollette (P.L. 78-113)	Broadened definition of eligibility to include people with mental illness and retardation; expanded services for physical restoration, living expenses and people who are blind.	1943

1

Laws	Emphasis	Year
Vocational Rehabilitation Act (P.L. 83-565) Hill-Burton Act	Authorized services for people with more severe disabilities, graduate training and research, and improving facilities at workshops and other rehabilitation settings.	1954
Vocational Rehabilitation Act (P.L. 89-333)	Authorized construction for rehabilitation facilities, established extended evaluation, and an expansion of services to all.	1965
Vocational Rehabilitation Act (P.L. 90-391)	Programs in vocational evaluation and work adjustment for "disadvantaged," services to families, and follow-up to employment.	1968
Vocational Rehabilitation Act (P.L. 93-112)	Emphasized services to people with more severe disabilities, involvement of consumers in rehabilitation process (IWRP), annual evaluations of eligibility, and programs of affirmative action and Individual Written Rehabilitation Plan (IWRP).	1973
Section 501:	Affirmative Action in Federal Hiring. Mandates nondiscrimination by the Federal Government in its own hiring practices.	
Section 502:	Architectural and Transportation Barriers Compliance. Insures compliance on accessibility of buildings constructed with federal funds.	
Section 503:	Affirmative Action by Federal Contract Recipients. Requires affirmative action on the part of all businesses that receive contracts from the Federal Government that exceed $2,500.	
Section 504:	Equal Opportunities. Prohibits the exclusion based on disability of otherwise qualified disabled persons from participation in any program or activity receiving federal financial assistance.	
Individuals with Disabilities Education Act (P.L. 94-142)	Mandated that states must provide education for all disabled children between the ages of 3 and 21. Includes rule of least restrictive environment. Also see IDEA (1997).	1975

Laws	Emphasis	Year
Rehabilitation, Comprehensive Services & Developmental Disabilities (P.L. 95-602)	Creates National Institute of Handicapped Research, new comprehensive rehabilitation centers, National Council on the Handicapped, independent living services, and continued emphasis of vocational services to people who have severe disabilities. Authorizes grants for American Indians for culturally relevant voc rehab (funded 1981).	1978
Rehabilitation Act Amendment (P.L. 99-506)	Addition of rehabilitation engineering and supported employment programs. Further enhanced in the Technology-Related Assistance for Individuals with Disabilities Act of 1988 (29 U.S.C. 2201(1)).	1986
Americans with Disabilities Act (ADA)	Prohibits discrimination against people with disabilities in employment, transportation, public accommodations, and activities of state and local government. Telecommunications relay services are established.	1990
Title I:	Employment. Employers with 15 or more employees may not discriminate against qualified individuals with disabilities. Key terms to know include qualified person with a disability, essential job functions, reasonable accommodation, and undue hardship.	
Title II:	Public Services. Part I - Public Bus Systems. New buses must be accessible. Paratransit must be provided to persons unable to use fixed route bus services. New bus stations and alterations to existing stations must be accessible. Part II - Public Rail Systems. New trains must be accessible. Already existing trains must have at least one accessible car. New train stations and alterations to existing stations must be accessible	
Title III:	Public Accommodations. Public accommodations (e.g. restaurants, hotels, pharmacies, stores, parks, private schools, day-care centers) may not discriminate on the basis of disability. Public accommodations must be accessible and provide auxiliary aids and services, unless undue burden would result.	

Title IV: Telecommunications. Companies offering telephone service to the general public must also offer telephone relay services (e.g. T.D.D.) to those who need it.

Title V: Miscellaneous. Includes insurance issues, congressional inclusion, and amendments to the Rehabilitation Act of 1973.

Direct Threat   A significant risk of substantial harm to the health or safety of the individual or others that cannot be eliminated or reduced by reasonable accommodation. The determination that an individual poses a "direct threat" shall be based on an individualized assessment of the individual's present ability to safely perform the essential functions of the job. This assessment shall be based on a reasonable medical judgment that relies on the most current medical knowledge and/or on the best available objective evidence. In determining whether an individual would post a direct threat, the factors to be considered include:

(1)   The duration of the risk;

(2)   The nature and severity of the potential harm;

(3)   The likelihood that the potential harm will occur; and

(4)   The imminence of the potential harm.

Disability   With respect to an individual, disability means:

(1)   A physical or mental impairment that substantially limits one or more of the major life activities of such individual;

(2)   A record of such impairment; or

(3)   Being regarded as having such an impairment.

Physical or mental impairment means:

(1)   Any psychological disorder, or condition, cosmetic disfigurement, or anatomical loss affecting one of the following body systems: neurological, musculoskeletal, special sense organs, respiratory (including speech organs), cardiovascular, reproductive, digestive, genitourinary, hemic and lymphatic, skin, and endocrine; or

(2) Any mental or psychological disorder, such as mental retardation, organic brain syndrome, emotional or mental illness, and specific learning disabilities.

Major life activities means functions such as caring for oneself, performing manual tasks, walking, seeing, hearing, speaking, breathing, learning, and working.

Is "regarded as having such an impairment" means:

(1) Has a physical or mental impairment that does not substantially limit major life activities but is treated by a covered entity as constituting such limitation;

(2) Has a physical or mental impairment that substantially limits major life activities only as a result of the attitudes of others toward such impairment; or

(3) Has none of the impairments defined in Paragraph (2) of this section but is treated by a covered entity as having a substantially limiting impairment.

Essential Functions Fundamental job duties of the employment position the individual with a disability holds or desires. Does not include the marginal functions of the position. A job function may be considered essential for any of several reasons, including but not limited to the following:

(1) The function may be essential because the reason the position exists is to perform the function.

(2) The function may be essential because of the limited number of employees available among whom the performance of that job function can be distributed; and/or

(3) The function may be highly specialized so that the incumbent in the position is hired for his or her expertise or ability to perform the particular function.

Evidence of whether a particular function is essential includes, but is not limited to:

(1) The employer's judgment as to which functions are essential;

(2)	Written job descriptions prepared before advertising or interviewing applicants for the job;
(3)	The amount of time spent on the job performing the function;
(4)	The consequence of not requiring the incumbent to perform the function;
(5)	The terms of a collective bargaining agreement;
(6)	The work experience of past incumbents in the job; and/or
(7)	The current work experience of incumbents in similar jobs.

Qualified
Individual
with
Disability

An individual with a disability who, with or without reasonable accommodations, can perform the essential functions of the employment position that such individual holds or desires. Consideration shall be given to the employer's judgment as to what functions of a job are essential, and if an employer has prepared a written description before advertising or interviewing applicants for the job, this description shall be considered evidence of the essential functions of the job.

Reasonable
Accommodation

(1) Modifications or adjustments to a job application process that enable a qualified applicant with a disability to be considered for the position such qualified applicant desires; or

(2) Modifications or adjustments to the work environment, or to the manner of circumstances under which the position held or desired is customarily performed, that enable the individual with a disability to perform the essential functions of that position; or

(3) Modifications or adjustments that enable a covered individual to enjoy equal benefits and privileges of employment as are enjoyed by its other similarly situated employees without disabilities.

Reasonable accommodation may include but is not limited to:

(1) Making existing facilities used by employees readily accessible to and usable by individuals with disabilities; and

(2) Job restructuring; part-time or modified work schedules; reassignment to a vacant position; acquisition or modifications

of equipment or devices; appropriate adjustment or modifications of examinations, training materials, or policies; the provision of qualified readers or interpreters; and other similar accommodations for individuals with disabilities.

To determine the appropriate reasonable accommodation, it may be necessary for the covered entity to initiate an informal, interactive process with a person with a disability in need of the accommodation. This process should identify the precise limitations resulting from the disability and potential reasonable accommodations that could overcome those limitations.

Substantially Limits

(1) Unable to perform a major life activity that the average person in the general population can perform; or

(2) Significantly restricted as to the condition, manner, or duration under which an individual can perform a particular major life activity as compared to the condition, manner, or duration under which the average person in the general population can perform that same major life activity.

(3) Significantly restricted in the ability to perform either a class of jobs or a broad range of jobs in various classes as compared to the average person having comparable training, skills, and abilities. The inability to perform a single, particular job does not constitute a substantial limitation in the major life activity of working.

Undue Hardship   An action requiring significant difficulty or expense, when considered in light of the factors set forth below. Factors to be considered include:

(1) the nature and cost of the accommodation needed under the Act;

(2) the overall financial resources of the facility or facilities involved in the provision of the reasonable accommodation; the number of persons employed at such facility; the effect of expenses and resources, or the impact otherwise of such accommodation upon the operation of the facility.

(3) the overall financial resources of the covered entity; the overall size of the business of a covered entity with respect to the number of its employees; the number, type, and location of its facilities; and

(4)   the type of operation or operations of the covered entity, including the composition, structure, and functions of the work force of such entity; the geographic separateness, administrative, or fiscal relationship of the facility or facilities in question to the covered entity.

Rehabilitation Amendments Of 1992	Established consumer rehabilitation advisory council for enhanced consumer input, research, and business. Provided for increased emphasis on severe mental illness. Also continued provisions for rehabilitation technology. Eligibility had to be established within 60 days of application. Clients were "empowered" and were to be intimately involved in the development and annual progress review of the Individual Plan for Employment (then known as Individualized Written Rehabilitation Plan – IWRP).
Individuals with Disabilities Education Act (P.L. 105-17) (1997)	Update of P.L. 94-142. Includes brain injury, autism and transition services (as of 1991). 1997 includes evaluations and curriculum requirements, procedural safeguards, discipline, early intervention and preschool services, teacher training and preparation.
Workforce Investment Act of 1998 (P. L. 105-220)	TITLE IV includes the Rehabilitation Act Amendments as amended from 1973. "To consolidate, coordinate, and improve employment, training, literacy, and vocational rehabilitation programs in the United States, and for other purposes." Includes provision for "one stop shopping." Also, consumer council became a strategic part of vocational rehabilitation planning (rather than "advisory"). IWRP became Individual Plan for Employment – IPE.
Carl D. Perkins Vocational and Technical Education Act of 1998 (P. L. 105-332)	The purpose of these funds is to assist schools in implementing programs that meet the Perkins Vocational and Applied Technology Education Act of 1998 (Perkins III) definition of career and technical education so that students will be prepared for high-demand, high-skill, high-wage occupations and postsecondary education.
Rehabilitation Amendments of 1998	Gave states the flexibility to locate vocational rehabilitation anywhere in the state organizational chart. Requires a state plan with an estimate of number of expected clients to be served, the costs, goals and priorities, strategies and reports of progress. Funding: Typically 78.7% federal, 21.3% state.

Native American Vocational Act	Funded through the Department of Education Carl Perkins Vocational Education Act. These programs provide in house training to disadvantaged adults. Focus on child care and business technology
Assistive Technology Act of 1998 (P.L. 105-394)	Continuation of funding of AT projects. Terms to know: Rehabilitation Engineering Centers ("RECs"); Rehabilitation Engineering Research Centers ("RERCs") (25 as of 2008). Emphasis on engineering to improve the quality of life for people with disabilities.

II.   Important Rehabilitation Research
    A.   Du Pont Studies
        Du Pont studies over a period of more than 25 years have shown that the performance of people with disabilities is equivalent or above their non-impaired co-workers in safety, performance of job duties and attendance.

III.   Important Names in the History of Rehabilitation

    A.   Thomas Gallaudet: Commitment to the improvement of opportunities for deaf and hearing impaired persons. Gallaudet College in Washington, D.C. established in 1864 to provide higher education for deaf persons needing special facilities to compensate for their loss of hearing.

    B.   Dorothea Dix: Commitment to the improvement of opportunities for persons with mental illness.

    C.   Samuel Howe: Committed to the improvement of opportunities for persons with mental retardation, visual impairments and/or blindness

    D.   Dr. Howard Rusk: Initiated organization of the first department of physical medicine and rehabilitation at the New York University Medical School.

    E.   Mary Switzer: Former Commissioner of Vocational Rehabilitation and a significant figure in the rehabilitation movement. Saw society in the early 1960s moving toward greater acceptance of the necessity of rehabilitation programs on moral grounds. The most coveted award in Rehabilitation is named for her.

    F.   Justin Dart: (1930-2002) Leader of the international disability rights movement and a renowned human rights activist. He contracted polio in 1948 and went on to develop a very successful business in the 1950s. In 1981, President Ronald Reagan appointed Dart to be the vice-chair of the National

Council on Disability. He was instrumental in drafting a national policy that called for national civil rights legislation to end the centuries old discrimination of people with disabilities which eventually became the Americans with Disabilities Act of 1990. In 1986, Dart was appointed to head the Rehabilitation Services Administration, a $3 billion federal agency that oversees a vast array of programs for disabled people. Dart called for radical changes, and for including people with disabilities in every aspect of designing, implementing, and monitoring rehabilitation programs. Resisted by the bureaucracy, Dart dropped a bombshell when he testified at a public hearing before Congress that the RSA was "a vast, inflexible federal system which, like the society it represents, still contains a significant portion of individuals who have not yet overcome obsolete, paternalistic attitudes about disability." Dart was asked to resign his position, but remained a supporter of both Presidents Reagan and Bush. In 1989, Dart was appointed chair of the President's Committee on the Employment of People with Disabilities, shifting its focus from its traditional stance of urging business to "hire the handicapped" to advocating for full civil rights for people with disabilities. Dart is best known for his work in passing the Americans with Disabilities Act of 1990 (from http://abilitymagazine.com/JustinDart_remembered.html).

IV.   Similarities and Differences Between Vocational Rehabilitation in the Public and
       Private Sectors

Differences
(Partial Listing)

Public	Private
Funded primarily by public money. Usually Fed/State matching.	Funded primarily through fee for services with occasional govt. contracts.
Usually staffed by vocational counselors.	Usually very diverse backgrounds including nurses, job development specialists, etc.
Wide variety of caseloads, e.g. developmental disabilities, learning disabled, congenital and medical disorders, emotionally disturbed, etc.	Primary caseload is with work injured.
Work setting is almost always a part of a large bureaucracy.	Most are associated with smaller companies (comparatively).
Vocational rehabilitation usually to the maximum potential.	Vocational rehabilitation to pre-injury wage level.
Clients must meet eligibility requirements.	No eligibility requirements and occasionally assist people with no disability.
Usually do not actively engage in medical management.	Frequently monitor medical progress.
Arrange for Basic medical and other diagnostic exams.	Usually do not require basic medical and often do not arrange diagnostic exams.

(Continued next page)

Public	Private
Case records must meet Fed/ State requirements.	Case recording generally reflects style of the individual company with occasional record similarities based on individual state requirements, or federal contract requirements.
Do not review medical bills for accuracy and correctness.	Some companies specialize in reviewing medical bills for accuracy.
Less actively involved in job placement, labor market survey, and related work.	Usually active in job placement labor market surveys and related activity.
Usually avoids expert testimony.	Often utilized as expert witness.
Caseloads often 100 or more.	Caseloads usually 20-30.
Less active in professional associations.	Usually very active in professional associations.
Salary not based on production.	Salary often partially based on commissions or production.
Promotions and wage increases usually weighted in favor of length of service.	Promotions heavily influenced by professional success.
Usually not actively involved with business practices such as time sheets or marketing.	Frequently involved with business practices such as time sheets and marketing.

Similarities
Overall there are probably more similarities than differences. Both are interested in the employment of persons with disabilities, represent similar attitudes and goals, practice counseling, evaluate, develop and write vocational plans, etc. Much of the research tends to indicate similar activities with differing emphasis. To reproduce them here would be beyond the scope of the table. (Chase, 1983, Field 1981, Matkin, 1980, Matkin, 1983, Rubin, Matkin, Ashley, Beardsley, May, Onstott, and Puckett, 1983, Sink, Porter, Rubin, Painter, 1979, Weed, 1981 as cited in Weed & Field, 2001, *Rehabilitation Consultant's Handbook*).

V.   Disability Management Movement

Disability Management is a relatively new concept, which empowers employers to minimize the impact of impairment resulting from injury, illness, or disease on the individual's capacity to participate competitively in the work environment. It is a process where labor and management assume joint responsibility as proactive decision makers, planners, and coordinators for work-based interventions and services. It also promotes disability prevention strategies and safe return to work programs.

As summarized on the Disability Management Certification website (www.cdms.org), the delivery of disability management services involves a complex interplay among workers with disabilities, employers, insurance carriers, labor unions, medical service providers, government agencies, and others.

- A major goal of disability management is to facilitate the worker's physical recovery, rehabilitation and return-to-work process while, concurrently, controlling the escalating costs of injury and disability for employers, insurance carriers and government.

- Within this context of competing interests, the disability management specialist must function in an objective and ethical fashion.

- The disability management specialist must maintain a balance between providing services and interventions that protect jobs for workers with disabilities while controlling the financial, safety and other risks that confront employers.

VI.   Case management (also see CRC scope of practice definitions later in this chapter)

Case management refers to the ability of the rehabilitation counselor to effectively manage the various aspects of the rehabilitation process. Core components include interviewing and working with the client, keeping relevant records/documentation, outreach, prescreening, assessment, monitoring, developing a plan of care, appropriate referral, and working with other agencies. Typically the successful rehabilitation counselor not only possesses excellent clinical skills, but also "case management" skills.

Case management refers to the counselor's managerial activities that facilitate the movement of the client through the rehabilitation process toward achieving specific client goals. This requires good organization and time management capabilities, as well as assuming the primary role of coordinator of services.

Initial interview core information includes age, gender, medical history, reported disabilities, functional abilities and limitations, work and educational history, family and support network, social functioning and economic resources.

Disability management refers to professionals who typically work with an employer to reduce on-the-job injuries or help effect return to work plans for employees injured while working. A disability manager may also provide case management services (also see section on disability management).

Source: Andrew, J. & Faubion, C. (Eds.) (2002). Rehabilitation Services: An introduction for the human services professional. Osage Beach, MO: Aspen.

VII. Independent Living (also see end of Chapter 2 for more information)

Authorized initially by the 1978 Rehabilitation Act and was administered by the State office of vocational rehabilitation. Now usually operated by Independent Living Centers and commonly staffed by "peers."

Funding primarily provided under Title VII, Part B of the Rehabilitation Act, which is administered through the Rehabilitation Services Administration under the U.S. Department of Education. Other funding obtained from United Way, corporations, foundations, government contracts, and private donations.

VIII.   Counselor-client relationships with multicultural and diversity issues and topics

- Attitudes towards those with disabilities show the following as major determinants of societal responses based on historical and contemporary reviews the literature.
  - Perceived cause of disability
  - Perceived responsibility for the disability
  - Perceived threat of the disability
  - Prevailing economic conditions within society
  - Prevailing sociocultural milieu

- In 1860's organic causes of disability became popular. This became the demise of moral treatment and the asylum movement and institutions became warehouses.
- During the 1960's society, capitalism and social institutions (such as the family) were blamed as the cause of mental illness. Institutions were seen has a hindrance to treatment of mental illness. Institutions were seen as a victimization process. The sociological approach lead to deinstitutionalization, normalization, and independent living movements
- Definitions that distinguish between disability and handicap reflect society's role. Persons with physical disability may be handicapped not by the fact that they use a wheelchair but because society chooses to use stairs instead of elevators or ramps
- Unemployment may occur not because of physical limitations, but because of employer prejudices and stereotypes
- Attitudes, economic, social and political structures and the physical environment are now recognized as the source of the handicap as opposed to the disability itself.
- Common employer concerns regarding hiring people with disabilities.

- Increases in worker's compensation rates
- Loss of productivity
- Increased absenteeism
- Costs of modifying the workplace or providing extra safety precautions

- Factors re the economy that influence societal responses to people with disabilities
  - The overall state of the economy
  - Functions in different components of the economy
  - Demand for labor
  - Level of inflation
  - Government revenue

- Importance of multicultural emphasis in counseling
  - Minorities are generally under served by counseling profession
  - Current counseling methods are from majority cultural perspective = lack efficacy
  - Minority clients are more prone to drop out or avoid counseling
  - Counseling viewed as way of maintaining status quo of oppression and control of minorities
  - Minority clients have more often found selves in position to be forced into counseling, i.e., court-ordered or school referred.

- N.Y. State Rehab Services records showed reason for client closure for Caucasians was typically client "refused services"; for minorities it was listed as "failure to cooperate."

- Ethnic and minorities with disabilities:
  - Have a disproportionately higher rate of rejection for rehab services
  - When accepted, are provided less effective services with poorer rehab outcomes

- Dziekan & Okocha (1993) reported racial and ethnic minorities applied for voc rehab services at a higher rate than general population but were accepted for services at lower rate than white applicants.

- Principals of multicultural counseling
  - Counselor should consider cultural variables as very real and very important
  - Cultural variables affect both counselor and client
  - Counselors become aware of their own cultural baggage
  - Counselors should respect culture of client
  - Become aware of any unique cultural characteristics and learn to value characteristics

- Multiculturalism holds value-free counseling to be a myth since both counselors and clients bring their own cultural values into the counseling interaction.

- The counselor should incorporate the client's perspective into counseling, and he/she needs to value client as an individual person and develop respect for their autonomy.
- Qualities of empathy are important.
- Respect for client individuality, autonomy and uniqueness.
- The counselor should be warm, accepting, and nonjudgmental.
- Societal values of independence, self-sufficiency, health, productivity, work, physical beauty and certain types of behavior are held by majority of Americans.
- Counselors should be aware that they may also hold these values and their attitudes can affect the counseling relationship and helping the client reach his or her goals.
- It is more important to focus on the actual limitations resulting from the disability and the psychological reactions these limitations cause than on the diagnostic terms.

- Four phases of rehabilitation process
  - Evaluation
  - Planning
  - Treatment
  - Termination

- It is important for rehabilitation counselors to develop a positive, facilitative relationship with the client.

IX.   Termination rates for minorities are higher than the majority
- 50% of minorities terminate after the first session.
- Ignored cultural and value differences, stereotypes contributed to the termination rate.
- Data show that women have a higher rate of disabilities than men in the general population.

X. Subgroup issues and topics

- AFRICAN AMERICANS
19.1 % of African American males have some type of disability compared to African American females with 21.7%. However, they are less likely to be accepted for service. African Americans have the highest rate of severe disabilities of all groups. Several factors contribute to this high rate including: unskilled work, dangerous conditions, and lack of access to adequate health care. Common health issues with African Americans include hypertension, heart disease and strokes.

- ASIAN AMERICAN
Asian Americans are one of the fastest growing minority groups. Counselors must become aware of the specific subgroups and how they are different. It is important to note that Asian families place a high priority on education. Traditional Western therapies may be difficult with Asian clients. First, Asian clients may see the counselor as an expert and

expect him/her to be directive and provide answers. Therapeutic issues such as insight and introspection are not valued in the Asian culture. The family must be involved in the rehabilitation plan. It is also important for the counselor to assess the Asian client's level of acculturation.

- HISPANIC/LATINO

The Hispanic/Latino population has grown faster than any other minority group in the U.S. This diverse group includes Cubans, Mexicans, Puerto Ricans, and other groups from South America. The most common element among the Hispanic population is the language. Hispanics have a lower rate of disabilities when compared to other groups. Hispanic women have a higher rate of disabilities than men. One of the major issues impacting the Hispanic is limited assess to adequate health care. When working with Hispanics, it is important to assess their level of acculturation. The use of an interpreter may be needed if the client has difficulty speaking English.

- NATIVE AMERICANS

Native Americans are 1% of the US population but rates of disabilities are disproportionately higher than other minority groups. Disability rates are higher than the national average. Dangerous working conditions, high unemployment & underemployment are some of the conditions that impact the Native American client. The leading causes of death include heart disease, auto accidents, diabetes and chronic liver disease. Alcoholism and suicide continue to have an impact in the Native American culture.

- WOMEN

Women continue to experience discrimination compared to males in the work place. Inequities in pay continue to exist even when women are employed in identical positions as men. Women experience disabilities at higher rates than men. Women with disabilities are more likely to be isolated and dependent on family members, friends or caregivers. Women of ethnic minority groups had even lower employment rates, made less money and were more likely to be in low status, low advancement jobs. Research data for female clients supported that they were under represented as applicants but had a higher rate of acceptance for service and successful case closure.

- Gay, Lesbian, Bisexual, and Transgender (GLBT) Americans

Although there is little literature on this research area, one source notes that GLBT persons are often the object of regular oppression in schools, organizations and communities. Reportedly they often experience beatings, isolation, ridicule and victimization as a result of their sexual identity and/or gender identification. Hence, there is substantial pressure to hide one's true feelings in this area.

The American Counseling Association's Code of Ethics promotes the use of a standardized language supporting the GLBT community. However, gender identity is not included in the list of definitions. Gender identity refers to the internal subjective experience with regard to gender roles, attitudes and behaviors. It may, or may not, match the person's genitalia, clothing or gender "signals or cues."

"Sexual orientation can be defined as a multivariate dynamic that includes past, present, and ideal feelings about who is attractive, or desirable, in a sexual or romantic way. It can include one's sexual attractions, behaviors, fantasies, gender emotional preference, gender social preference, sexual identity in a community, and use of a sexual identity self label" (p. 337).

Source: Poole, K. & Robertson, J. (2002). Multiculturalism in rehabilitation: The changing faces of diversity. In J. Andrew & C. Faubion (Eds.) *Rehabilitation Services: An introduction for the human services professional* (pp. 329-339). Osage Beach, MO: Aspen.

A second source suggests:
Rehabilitation counselors who works with GLBT clients should be aware of and acknowledge any personal bias or prejudice toward theses individuals. The counselor is encouraged to communicate with the GLBT client in an ethical, professional, and straightforward manner. It is imperative that counselors get to know the client as an individual who deserves respect, compassion and high quality service. Any attempts to convince the client that he/she is not homosexual or could benefit from reparative therapy may invite an ethical complaint. (Dr. Barry Chung, personal communication, June 17, 2004)

XI.   Certified Rehabilitation Counselor (CRC) knowledge areas and exam question relevance.

12 knowledge domains represent a valid "core" of the types of knowledge and skills needed for rehabilitation counseling practice (http://www.crccertification.com/ downloads/10certification2/A/01-20080411CRC_Certification_Guide.doc):

1.   Career Counseling and Assessment
   - Theories of career development and work adjustment
   - Tests and evaluation techniques for assessing clients
   - Psychometric concepts related to measurement
   - Interpretation of assessment results for rehabilitation planning purposes
   - Computer- and Internet-based career resources
   - Transferable skills analysis
   - Assistive technology

2.   Job Development and Placement Services
   - Vocational implications of functional limitations
   - Job readiness including seeking and retention skills

- Techniques used to conduct labor market surveys
- Occupational and labor market information
- Job matching strategies
- Employer development for job placement
- Employment support services
- Employment settings

3. Vocational Consultation and Services for Employers
- Employer practices that affect the employment or return to work of individuals with disabilities
- Marketing rehabilitation services and benefits for employers
- Educating employers on disability-related issues
- Disability prevention and management strategies
- Job analysis and/or job description development
- Job modification, accommodation, and restructuring including ergonomic assessment
- Work conditioning or work hardening resources and strategies

4. Case and Caseload Management
- Case management process, including time management and prioritization, rehabilitation planning, service coordination, and referral to and collaboration with other disciplines
- Principles of caseload management including case recording and documentation
- Professional roles, responsibilities, functions, and relationships with clients and other human service providers
- Negotiation, mediation, and conflict resolution strategies
- Techniques for working effectively in teams and across disciplines

5. Individual Counseling
- Individual counseling theories
- Individual counseling practices and interventions
- Behavior and personality theory
- Human growth and development
- Multicultural counseling theories and practices related to individual counseling

6. Group and Family Counseling
- Family counseling theories
- Family counseling practices and interventions
- Group counseling theories
- Group counseling practices and interventions
- Multicultural counseling theories and practices related to group and family counseling

7. Mental Health Counseling
   - Diagnostic and Statistical Manual
   - Rehabilitation techniques for individuals with psychiatric disabilities
   - Multicultural counseling theories and practices related to mental health counseling
   - Medications as they apply to individuals with psychiatric disabilities
   - Dual diagnosis
   - Substance abuse
   - Treatment planning
   - Wellness and illness prevention concepts and strategies

8. Psychosocial and Cultural Issues in Counseling
   - Individual and family adjustment to disability
   - Psychosocial and cultural impact of disability on the individual
   - Psychosocial and cultural impact of disability on the family
   - Attitudinal barriers for individuals with disabilities
   - Societal issues, trends, and developments as they relate to rehabilitation
   - Working with individuals from various socioeconomic backgrounds
   - Working with individuals with English as a second language
   - Gender issues
   - Human sexuality and disability issues

9. Medical, Functional, and Environmental Aspects of Disabilities
   - Medical aspects and implications of various disabilities
   - Medical terminology
   - Medications as they relate to vocational goals and outcomes
   - Functional capacities of individuals with physical, psychiatric, and/or cognitive disabilities
   - Environmental barriers for individuals with disabilities
   - Rehabilitation terminology and concepts

10. Foundations, Ethics, and Professional Issues
   - Philosophical foundations of rehabilitation
   - Legislation or laws affecting individuals with disabilities
   - Ethical decision making models and processes
   - Ethical standards for rehabilitation counselors
   - Advocacy for individuals with disabilities
   - Theories and techniques for providing clinical supervision
   - Interpretation and application of research findings
   - Evaluation procedures for assessing the effectiveness of rehabilitation services, programs, and outcomes

11. Rehabilitation Services and Resources
   - Financial support/funding resources for rehabilitation services and programs
   - Organizations/programs providing rehabilitation services
   - Community referral resources and services for rehabilitation planning
   - Services available from one-stop career centers
   - Services available relating to ergonomics, assistive technology, kinesiology and rehabilitation engineering
   - Services available through client advocacy programs
   - Programs for specialty populations
   - Forensic rehabilitation services

12. Healthcare and Disability Systems
   - Managed care concepts
   - Insurance programs
   - Health care benefits
   - Workers' compensation laws and practices
   - Social Security programs, benefits, work incentives, and disincentives

XII.   Scope of rehabilitation counseling practice (CRC)
Source: Commission on Rehabilitation Counselor Certification. (2003). *Scope of Practice for Rehabilitation Counseling.* Retrieved May 6, 2008 from, http://www.crccertification.com/pages/31research.html

The specific techniques and modalities utilized within the rehabilitation counseling process may include, but are not limited to:

   - Assessment and appraisal;

   - Diagnosis and treatment planning;

   - Career (vocational) counseling;

   - Individual and group counseling treatment interventions focused on facilitating adjustments to the medical and psychosocial impact of disability;

   - Case management, referral, and service coordination;

   - Program evaluation and research;

   - Interventions to remove environmental, employment, and attitudinal barriers;

   - Consultation services among multiple parties and regulatory systems;

   - Job analysis, job development, and placement services, including assistance with employment and job accommodations; and

   - The provision of consultation about and access to rehabilitation technology.

The following definitions are related to the Scope of Practice Statement for Rehabilitation Counseling.

Appraisal: Selecting, administering, scoring, and interpreting instruments designed to assess an individual's aptitudes, abilities, achievements, interests, personal characteristics, disabilities, and mental, emotional, or behavioral disorders as well as the use of methods and techniques for understanding human behavior in relation to coping with, adapting to, or changing life situations.

Diagnosis and Treatment Planning: Assessing, analyzing, and providing diagnostic descriptions of mental, emotional, or behavioral conditions or disabilities; exploring possible solutions; and developing and implementing a treatment plan for mental, emotional, and psychosocial adjustment or development. Diagnosis and treatment planning shall not be construed to permit the performance of any act that rehabilitation counselors are not educated and trained to perform.

Counseling Treatment Intervention: The application of cognitive, affective, behavioral, and systemic counseling strategies which includes developmental, wellness, pathologic, and multicultural principles of human behavior. Such interventions are specifically implemented in the context of a professional counseling relationship and may include, but are not limited to: appraisal; individual, group, marriage, and family counseling and psychotherapy; the diagnostic description and treatment of persons with mental, emotional, and behavioral disorders or disabilities; guidance and consulting to facilitate normal growth and development, including educational and career development; the utilization of functional assessments and career counseling for persons requesting assistance in adjusting to a disability or handicapping condition; referrals; consulting; and research.

Referral: Evaluating and identifying the needs of a client to determine the advisability of referrals to other specialists, advising the client of such judgments, and communicating as requested or deemed appropriate to such referral sources.

Case Management: A systematic process merging counseling and managerial concepts and skills through the application of techniques derived from intuitive and researched methods, thereby advancing efficient and effective decision-making for functional control of self, client, setting, and other relevant factors for anchoring a proactive practice. In case management, the counselor's role is focused on interviewing, counseling, planning rehabilitation programs, coordinating services, interacting with significant others, placing clients and following up with them, monitoring progress, and solving problems.

Program Evaluation: The effort to determine what changes occur as a result of a planned program by comparing actual changes (results) with desired changes (stated goals), and by identifying the degree to which the activity (planned program) is responsible for those changes.

Research: A systematic effort to collect, analyze, and interpret quantitative or qualitative data that describe how social characteristics, behavior, emotions, cognition, disabilities, mental disorders, and interpersonal transactions among individuals and organizations interact.

Consultation: The application of scientific principles and procedures in counseling and human development to provide assistance in understanding and solving current or potential problems that the consultee may have in relation to a third party, be it an individual, group, or organization.

XIII.   General Ethics Topics
       Professional ethics are designed to protect the public.
a. Major tenets include:
- Do no harm
- Protect the public

b. Professional ethics provide a guideline for professional behavior.

c. Five major ethical principles:
- Beneficence - doing good and preventing harm
- Nonmalfeasance - not inflicting harm, identifying interventions that are least likely to result in harm or injury to the client.
- Justice - fairness
- Autonomy - client's freedom of choice and right to self-determination.
- Fidelity - keeping promises and commitments that counselor has made to clients.

d. CRC Code of Ethics (Sent to you as part of the application) (NOTE: in 2008, the CRC ethics document has been revised, thought not published at the time of this publication)
       A review of the CRC code of ethics is strongly recommended. Items on the CRC examination related to ethical decision making typically consist of long scenarios. The examiner has to make a choice between alternatives to resolve the dilemma or identify the ethical principal associated with the scenario. It is extremely important that you carefully read and understand the question.

XIV. Unbiased language aka Disability Etiquette

In a one page outline titled *Words that Empower*, about unbiased language from the President's Committee for the Employment of Persons with Disabilities, the following guidelines are offered.

- People with disabilities should be treated with dignity and respect. Everyone has different personalities and preferences. To find out what the person desires or prefers, ask them.

- When you meet someone with a disability, it is appropriate to shake hands, even if a person has limited use or artificial limbs. Simply touch hands (or the person's prosthesis) to acknowledge his/her presence. Shaking the left hand is also fine.

- Before assisting a person with a disability ask them. They may not want help. If they do, listen carefully to instructions. For example, before you push someone's wheelchair, ask if they need help. Likewise, never move crutches or communication boards out of the owner's reach without permission.

- Be considerate of how long it takes to get certain things done.

- Speak directly to the person with a disability rather than to a companion or sign language interpreter.

- Do not pet a service dog without permission.

- Some terms that might have sounded acceptable in the past, such as "crippled," "deaf and dumb," and "wheelchair-bound" are no longer acceptable because of negative connotations. Instead say "person with a disability," "Mary has deafness or hard of hearing" (note: some also take offense to using the words "hearing impaired"),"Denise uses a wheelchair," and "Joe has mental retardation." This type of language focuses on the person first, and his or her disability afterwards. (See "Words that Empower" below.)

- Avoid excessive praise when people with disabilities accomplish normal tasks. Living with a disability is an adjustment and does not require exaggerated compliments.

Words That Empower (negative phrase followed by affirmative phrase)

- Instead of "the disabled, the handicapped, crippled" say "person with a disability."

- If a person relies on a wheelchair, do not say "confined to a wheelchair" or if the person uses a power chair do not say they use an "electric chair" which gives the image of criminal consequence.

- Rather than "suffers a hearing loss" say "person with a hearing loss."

- Avoid "afflicted or stricken by MS, MD, CP, etc." say "person with MS, MD, CP, etc."

- Instead of "epileptic" say "person with epilepsy." Or instead of they had an "epileptic fit' rephrase to "seizure."

- Rather than "normal person" which implies person with a disability isn't normal, say "temporarily able-bodied or person who does not have a disability."

- Instead of "crippled, lame, deformed' say "disabled."

- Rather than 'crazy or nuts" refer to the person as someone with "mental disabilities."

- Avoid "admits she has a disability" since it implies guilt or shame.

- Avoid saying that a person with a disability is "courageous" since many people with disabilities do not feel as if the disability is anything to overcome. For example, many people who are unable to hear consider themselves to be similar to people from a different culture and not someone with a disability.

I.   The Vocational Rehabilitation Process

   A.   Determination of Eligibility for a State/Federal Program

         The following 3 criteria must be met:

         1.   Individual must have a disability.

         2.   The disability impacts the ability to work.

         3.   The individual can and wants to work, and can benefit from services.

         * "Presumptive eligibility." An individual receiving SSI/SSDI is presumed to be eligible for, and able to benefit from, vocational rehabilitation services.

   B.   Justification for Public Sector Rehabilitation

         Funds made possible through taxes are used to assist persons with disabilities to prepare for, engage in, and retain gainful employment. Once gainfully employed, clients no longer rely on vocational services and become taxpayers, thus "paying back" the cost of their services. Historically tax dollars returned from earnings of clients following rehabilitation services outweighs the cost. Some studies indicate for every dollar spent about $11 are returned through taxes.

   C.   Client Assistant Program (CAP)

         Originally patterned after the Developmental Disabilities Protection and Advocacy Program, CAP serves to advocate on behalf of public sector rehabilitation clients.

   D.   Individual Plan for Employment (or IPE) (Note: the exam may use the old nomenclature of Individualized Written Rehabilitation Plan or IWRP)

         1.   Identifies aspects inherent to the provision of rehabilitation services.

         2.   Serves as a contract between the client and counselor.

         3.   Can be amended by client and counselor at any time.

         4.   Client must understand and be involved in the formation of the IPE.

         5.   The IPE includes:

               a.   Basis on which determination of eligibility was made.

b.   Assurance that client has been informed of client rights.

c.   Long-term goals and immediate rehabilitation objectives.

d.   Services to be provided.

e.   Projected date for initiation of each service.

f.   Responsibilities of client.

g.   Financial responsibilities for services to be provided.

h.   Procedure for evaluation.

i.   Post-employment services, if planned at time of closure.

Note: Sheltered employment is no longer an acceptable goal.

E.   Client Rights

1.   Clients must have a voice in matters that affect them.

2.   Clients must have authority over their own destinies.

3.   Advisory groups of public agencies must include consumer representation.

4.   Clients must participate in their own planning for services and approve of the plan.

5.   Confidentiality

Disclosures of the client to the professional will not be revealed to others except under certain circumstances.

6.   Privileged Communication

Granted by statute to protect a client's confidential communication with a professional from being disclosed against the client's will in a legal proceeding. Unless the client has waived his or her rights, he or she has the privilege of preventing the professional from answering questions about their communication when the professional is called as a witness in court. The client is free to waive this right.

7.   Advocate Counseling

Helps clients develop assertive skills that will enable them to improve their interactions with individuals and institutions. Emphasizes teaching and helping clients to advocate for themselves.

F.   Initial Interview

    1.   Develop a relationship with the client.

    2.   Complete evaluation of the client and document the disabling condition and how it impacts work. The purpose is to help determine the level of education, aptitude, and vocational functioning that a person possesses (Residual Functional Capacity).

    3.   Initiate determination as to the eligibility of the individual for rehabilitation services.

    4.   Begin assessment procedures (vocational evaluation, psychological assessment, physical capacities evaluation and medical evaluators as appropriate).

    5.   Planning and provision of rehabilitation services for the IPE

G.   Case Weighing

Used in public sector rehabilitation to give people with the most severe disability priority when funds are limited.

H.   General flow: Referral, Service Planning, Delivery of Services, Closure.

I.   Public Sector "status codes" (Also see appendix 1 for chart version.)

Status Code	Description
00	Referral, attempt to contact and take VR application
02	VR application filed, general diagnostic and evaluation-medical examination to determine eligibility for VR; psychological testing
04	This code is sometimes used as a "waiting list"
06	Extended evaluation up to 18 months of evaluation services to determine eligibility for VR (possibly in workshop or rehabilitation center)
08	Closed from categories 00, 02 or 06 as unsuccessful

10	Client determined eligible for VR services; client and counselor developing a rehabilitation plan including a vocational objective
12	Work plan completed and approved
14	Counseling and guidance
16	Physical restoration
18	Training (vocational, college, etc.)
20	Ready to work
22	Working
24	Services interrupted
26	**Rehabilitated** (Probably the most important status code to know. Must be in employment 90+ days.)
28	Closed from categories 14, 16, 18, 20, 22 as unsuccessful
30	Closed not rehabilitated (from status codes 10 and 12)
32	Receiving post-employment services. Used to assist a person to retain, regain or advance in employment
33	Terminated from post-employment services to enter employment status
35	Terminated from post-employment services; Continuing in employment

| 37 | Terminated from post-employment services; Not continuing in employment |
| 38 | Closed from Status 04 (client requests closure of the client is not eligible for services Many no longer use status 04 |

II. Transferability Process (skills are learned by doing – not to be confused with worker traits)

    A.   Vocational Diagnosis and Assessment of Residual Employability (VDARE) (Transferability of Worker Traits; a prelude to transferability of skills)

        A systematic and orderly method by which a vocational professional can evaluate a client's potential for work utilizing Department of Labor's data that is published in various forms. Some data are included in the Dictionary of Occupational Titles (DOT). Complete worker trait data is available in the Classification of Jobs (Field & Field, 2004, http://www.elliottfitzpatrick.com/ publications/#occupational) and other privately produced software/publications.

    B.   Prevocational Profile (PVP)

        Developed by tracing the client's work history experiences through the DOT to derive a qualifications profile for each job and then merging them all together. Indicates the client's highest level of demonstrated achievement.

    C.   Residual Functional Capacity (RFC)

        Modified PVP to reflect medical, psychological, social, educational, and vocational functioning. Indicates the client's current vocational potential.

    D.   Job Analysis

        1.   Formal process for observing jobs

        2.   Collect descriptive data about jobs from workers, employers, and observation

        3.   Translate these data into a standardized set of traits required of workers performing these jobs

        4.   Provides systematic and detailed information about a job including:

            a.   What the worker does in relation to data, people, and things

b. Methodology and techniques employed

c. Machines, tools, equipment, and work aids used

d. Materials, products, subject matter, or services that result

e. Traits required of the worker

5. When conducting a job analysis, inform the job supervisor in advance to avoid interruptions with workers during the observation period.

6. Selective job placement of individuals with disabilities may require that the rehabilitation counselor do a job analysis by gaining a first-hand awareness of the activities and surroundings of the work including:

a. Job tasks

b. Physical demands

c. Job methods

d. Working conditions

e. Job purpose

f. Hazards

g. Supervisory responsibilities

h. Job knowledge requirements

i. Mental application

j. Dexterity and accuracy requirements

k. Required experience

l. Required training

III. Arrangements/Codes

A. Guide to Occupational Exploration (GOE)

1. Job titles clustered by 12 categories of _interests_ which are further subdivided.

2. Good for career exploration.

B.   Industrial Designation (ID)

    1.   Jobs arranged by work activity or product.

    2.   Found in the Classification of Jobs (COJ).

C.   Materials, Products, Subject Matter and Services (MPSMS)

Jobs clustered by similarity to materials, products, subject matter, and services.

D.   Work Fields (WF)

    1.   Relates to the purpose of the job and how the job gets done.

    2.   Useful in counseling and guidance activities.

E.   Census

Jobs identified and representative of all jobs in the U.S. economy.

F.   Standard Occupational Classification (SOC)

Arrangement used for job surveys primarily in the manufacturing industries (unskilled/semi-skilled).

G.   Standard Industrial Classification (SIC)

Classification of business, industrial or manufacturing according to the type of activity that is performed at each setting. Used for job analysis and surveys.

H.   Guide to Job Analysis or Handbook for Analyzing Jobs

Federal definitions and detailed instructions for conducting job analysis.

I.   Occupational Outlook Handbook (OOH) (http://stats.bls.gov/ocohome.htm)

Jobs arranged by title, salary, and labor market.

Revised every two years, the *Handbook* describes what workers do on the job, working conditions, the training and education needed, earnings, and expected job prospects in a wide range of occupations

J.   O*NET, the online occupational network intended to replace the DOT
(below)

- Comprehensive Internet data base of worker attributes and job characteristics
- Designed around core information
- Uses a common language by describing worker attributes and workplace requirements
- Terms describe KSAs, interests, content and context of work to understand what is involved in effective job performance
- Database contains information re:
  - Knowledge, skills and abilities (KSAs)
  - Interests
  - General work abilities (GWAs)
  - Work context
- Developed based on the content model
- Consists of 6 major domains
  - Experience requirements = training, experience, licensing
  - Occupation requirements = generalized work activities, work content, organizational context
  - Occupation specific = occupational knowledges, occupational skills, tasks, machines, tools and equipment
  - Occupational characteristics = labor market information, occupational outlook, wages
  - Worker characteristics = abilities, interests and worker styles
  - worker requirements = basic skills, cross-functional skills, general knowledge and education

IV.   Dictionary of Occupational Titles (DOT) 4th edition

A.   Published by U.S. Dept. of Labor in 1977; revised in 1991. Will eventually be replaced by the O*NET. However, for forensic and Social Security Disability Insurance the O*NET is not adequate (as of 2004) and the DOT continues in use for "transferable skills analysis."

B.   Includes an occupational code for each job

1. First 3 digits - CATEGORY - DIVISION - GROUP

2. Middle 3 digits - DATA - PEOPLE - THINGS

3. Last 3 digits - alphabetical order of titles sharing the same first and middle sets of digits. If a 6 digit code is applicable to only one occupational title, the final 3 digits are always 010.

PARTS OF DOT CODE

1st 3 DIGITS	2nd 3 DIGITS	LAST 3 DIGITS
OCCUPATIONAL GROUP ARRANGEMENTS	WORKER FUNCTIONS (DATA, PEOPLE AND THINGS)	SERIAL # (ARRANGED BY # IN ALPHABETIC ORDER)
7 8 1	**6 8 4**	**0 3 0**
CATEGORY | DIVISION | GROUP	DATA | PEOPLE | THINGS	

V. Classification of Jobs (COJ)
Includes all occupational titles from the DOT and includes:

A. Physical demands

1. Lifting, carrying, pushing and/or pulling

   Sedentary (S) - 10 lbs. maximum

   Light   (L) - 20 lbs. maximum

   Medium   (M) - 50 lbs. maximum

   Heavy   (H) - 100 lbs. maximum

   Very Heavy (V) - lifting in excess of 100 lbs.

2. Climbing and/or balancing

3. Reaching, handling, fingering and/or feeling

4. Stooping, kneeling, crouching and/or crawling

5. Talking and/or hearing

6. Seeing

B.   Working Conditions

    1.   Inside, outside, or both

    2.   Extremes of cold plus temperature changes

    3.   Extremes of heat plus temperature changes

    4.   Wet and humid

    5.   Noise and vibration

    6.   Hazards

    7.   Fumes, odors, toxic conditions, dust, poor ventilation

C.   General Education Development (GED)

Scored on a scale of 1-6, 6 being the highest.

    1.   Reasoning

    2.   Math

    3.   Language

D.   Specific Vocational Preparation (SVP)

    1.   The amount of time necessary to learn the required techniques. (See following table)

Level	Time
1.	Short demonstration only.
2.	Anything beyond short demonstration up to and including thirty days.
3.	Over thirty days up to and including three months.
4.	Over three months up to and including six months.
5.	Over six months up to and including one year.
6.	Over one year up to and including two years.
7.	Over two years up to and including four years.
8.	Over four years up to and including ten years.
9.	Over ten years.

*   Levels 1 and 2 are considered unskilled
**   Levels 3 and 4 are considered semi-skilled

***   Levels 5 through 7 are considered skilled
****   Levels 8 and 9 are considered highly skilled

        E.   Aptitudes

             1.   Taken from General Aptitude Test Battery (GATB)/worker traits

G -	Intelligence
V -	Verbal
N -	Numerical
S -	Spatial
P -	Form Perception
Q -	Clerical Perception
K -	Motor Coordination
F -	Finger Dexterity
M -	Manual Dexterity
E -	Eye-Hand-Foot Coordination
C -	Color Discrimination

             2.   Scored on the following scale:

bottom 10%	bottom 1/3 not including the lowest 10%	middle 3rd	top 3rd not including the top 10%	top 10%
5	4	3	2	1

        F.   Interests

        G.   Temperaments

VI.   Job Development

        A.   Developing job opportunities for hard-to-place rehabilitation clients.

        B.   Continuing mutually beneficial relationships with community employers.

C. Providing clients with a chance for a career as opposed to temporary or substandard employment.

D. Goals of job development:

    1. Increase quality and quantity of worker productivity

    2. Reduce production costs

    3. Decrease labor turnover

    4. Lower accident rates

    5. Reduce sickness and absenteeism

    6. Improve worker morale and job satisfaction

E. Includes:

    1. Job solicitation

    2. Employer involvement

    3. Survey information

    4. Knowledge of community and business information, labor market information, and community patterns of influence

    5. Familiarity with business practice

F. Advantages to employers:

    1. Pre-screening for employers

    2. Training

    3. Selective placement

    4. Job modification

    5. Follow-up

VII.   Supported Employment

   A.   Goal: Competitive employment in an integrated work setting, or employment in an integrated work setting in which an individual is working toward competitive employment consistent with the strengths, resources, priorities, concerns, abilities, capabilities, interests, and informed choice of the individual.

   B.   A combination of employment, on-the-job training, and post-employment support used to place and maintain individuals with disabilities in competitive employment.

   C.   A job coach trains the individual on the job until performance criteria are met. The job coach may be needed for an extended period of time.

   D.   Support services offered by the job coach may also include counseling, job modification, social training, skill instruction, advocacy, and co-worker education.

   E.   Most often used with people with developmentally disabilities (e.g., clients with mentally retardation, autism, cerebral palsy), cognitive impaired (brain injury) and psychological disorders.

VIII. Workers' Compensation

   A.   The amount of compensation that workers receive for their disabilities incurred while on the job which is usually computed on a percentage of their weekly wage rate (usually 2/3 of former pay).

   B.   Purpose of workers' compensation laws:

      1.   To provide prompt, reasonable income and medical benefits to work-accident individuals, or income benefits to their dependents.

      2.   To eliminate payment of fees to lawyers and witnesses and time-consuming trials.

      3.   To encourage safety in the work place.

      4.   To promote study of accidents in order to reduce preventable accidents.

   C.   Imported from Germany and Austria

   D.   Began in the U.S. in Maryland (1902) and federal government in 1908.

   E.   Separate laws and regulations in each state. There is no federal mandate.

F.   Worker's Compensation rates are determined by:

     1.   Relative hazards in a company's work (e.g., office work is less hazardous than working as a roofer).

     2.   Company's accident experience.

     *This formula for determining premium rates does not consider the kind of personnel hired.

G.   Second Injury Protection or Subsequent Injury Fund

     1.   Protects employer from excessive claims for permanent total disability when an occupational injury is superimposed upon a pre-existing disability of an employee.

     2.   The employer is assessed only with costs of the second injury.

     3.   The assessment for total disability is spread among all employers by charging it to a second injury/subsequent injury fund.

     4.   Does not protect the new employer from a new injury.

H.   Types of Disability as Defined by Workers Compensation:

     1.   Temporary Total Disability (TTD).

     The individual is totally unable to return to work for a temporary period of time (e.g. A truck driver with a broken left foot).

     2.   Temporary Partial Disability (TPD).

     The individual is able to continue work on the job although there will be a temporary reduction in his/her performance on some job duties (e.g. A secretary with a herniated disc).

     3.   Permanent Partial Disability (PPD).

     There is a permanent disabling condition for the remainder of the individual's life, although the injury is only partially disabling. Person can continue working, although there will be a reduced level of functional capacity (e.g. A factory worker with an amputated leg).

     4.   Permanent and Total Disability (P&T).

     The worker is totally disabled for life (e.g., a laborer who becomes a ventilator tetraplegic).

I.   The Guide to Permanent Impairment

Determines the percentage of impairment that has been incurred.

1.   "Scheduled" Injury: an injury that is clearly associated with a given loss of function. Listed in a "schedule" in the workers comp law (e.g., amputated arm, or loss of an eye).

2.   "Unscheduled" Injury: an injury with ambiguous loss of function (e.g., low back or head injuries).

3.   Maximum Medical Improvement (MMI)

The plateau of improvement after all rehabilitative interventions have occurred. The client is not expected to improve with further treatment.

J.   Return to work hierarchy (General – can vary from State to State)

1.   Same employer/same job

2.   Same employer/different job

3.   Different employer/different job

4.   Training for new job

5.   Self employment

IX.   Forensic rehabilitation (personal injury litigation or court room related)

A.   Expert Witness

A witness shown to possess scientific, technical, or other specialized knowledge sufficient to show the court that she/he is an expert in a particular area. A witness may be qualified by any one or combination of the following factors: knowledge, skill, experience, training, or education. An expert need not have formal training.

B.   Subpoena

A formal "legal" request for records or appearance at a deposition or trial. If you receive a subpoena for confidential records of one of your clients, keep in mind that a subpoena for records is typically not reviewed by a judge for appropriateness. If you do not have a records release by the client it is best to check with your attorney before releasing them. Generally it is best for the rehabilitation professional to agree to provide the information once the appropriateness is determined. This is accomplished by writing to the attorney who requested or subpoenaed the information and explaining that as soon as proper releases or a judge's order is received the information will be provided promptly. (Note: One exam question reportedly refers to a judge issued subpoena. Typically a judge would issue a court order. The question may be confusing and the answer is apparently not technically among the choices.)

C. Rules of Evidence (litigation or court room related rehabilitation opinions)

When a rehabilitation counselor testifies, in most courtrooms, they must adhere to Rules of Evidence (see Federal Rules 702 and 703).

702
A witness qualified as an expert by knowledge, skill, experience, training, or education may testify thereto in the form of an opinion or otherwise.
- The opinion must be relevant to case.
- Court can provide wide latitude.
- Does not have to be based on first hand knowledge or observation.

703
Based on facts or data that are of a type reasonably relied on by experts in the particular field in forming opinions or inferences.

The rehabilitation expert witness must avoid hearsay and speculation. However, they can rely upon verbal facts and data that professionals in the rehabilitation field normally rely upon (if so, then it is not considered hearsay). For example, physician recommendations, cost research by contacting vendors, psychological diagnosis, vocational evaluations, etc.

D. Daubert and Kumho Tire Rulings (for litigation related rehabilitation settings)
(Daubert v Merrell Dow (1993) 125 L Ed 2d 469
Kumho Tire v Patrick Carmichael March 23, 1999, U.S. Supreme Court # 97-1709)

Basic Issues
- The judge MAY act as gatekeeper for allowing expert testimony
- Judge can not abuse discretion

Daubert/Kumho Tire Factors include:
- Testing (can theory be tested)
- Peer review/published
- Error rates (standards)
- Acceptability (general acceptance)
- Can throw out if discipline is unreliable (e.g., astrology)
- Kumho ruling supports the judge's decision to extend discretion to non-scientists.

- Bottom line: Rehabilitation experts who provide earnings capacity and future care recommendation opinions must show that they use procedures and methods that others in the field endorse. This can be accomplished by utilizing textbooks and articles to justify the approach. Giving an opinion "based on my education and experience" is not an adequate foundation.

X. Social Security Benefits

A. Social Security Disability Insurance (SSDI)

You pay taxes into the system during your working years (Social Security is taken out of your paycheck), and then you receive monthly benefits if/when you become unable to work. Disability is defined as a mental or physical impairment that is expected to keep the individual from performing substantial gainful activity for at least one year or is expected to result in death.

SSDI begins during the sixth full month of disability. After 24 months of receiving SSDI, most persons are also eligible for Medicare health insurance.

SSDI also provides for work incentives. A trial work period is allowed for the first nine months where full benefits are continued. If a person loses his or her job during the first 24 months, benefits can be restarted without having to re-apply.

B. Supplemental Security Income (SSI)

Monthly payments to people who have low income and few assets. (Usually people under the age of 18, or adults with limited work history). Persons receiving SSI are also usually eligible for Medicaid health insurance.

To qualify for SSI you must have a physical or mental impairment that is expected to keep you from doing any substantial work for at least one year. Or, you must have a condition that is expected to result in your death.

Work incentives are also available. Earned income exclusion, student earned income exclusion (under the age of 22), and blind work expenses are examples.

A "plan for achieving self support" (PASS) can allow for a deduction for impairment related work expenses such as personal care assistance, medical supplies, or modifications to a vehicle.

Property essential for self-support (PESS) allows the value of property essential to a job to be excluded as assets for Medicaid/SSI.

XI.   Workshops

The workshop is the most realistic substitute for work in industry yet devised to:

1.   Test the ability of individuals with disabilities to work.

2.   To provide income from non-profit employment.

3.   To assist in maintaining their well-being.

However, this is no longer a job goal for people receiving vocational rehabilitation services from a state agency.

A.   Rehabilitation Workshop

1.   A controlled working environment with individualized goals that permit persons with a disability to work at their own capacity and to be paid accordingly.

2.   Operates as a business in that it raises funds by product sales and other means to cover overhead expenses. Workers are paid wages.

3.   Operates as a human service agency, provides supportive services to its workers as clients, providing them with assessment, training, and assistance in finding jobs outside of the workshop

B.   Transitional Workshop

1.   A short-term workshop in which the emphasis is on placement from here to competitive employment or a sheltered workshop.

2.   Offers vocational exploration and intensive training (work hardening, work habits, work tolerance, and work performance).

C.   Sheltered Workshop

1.   The emphasis is on substantial employment for those who appear unable to return to work in the open labor market.

2.   Clients are employed, earning money, and contributing to their own and their family's support although wages and production are somewhat below competitive business levels.

3.   Employment in a sheltered workshop may lead to competitive employment even though this may take years.

4.   As a result of being employed in a sheltered workshop, clients have the opportunity to improve or maintain their self-worth.

XII.   Vocational Counseling Terms

A.   Occupational Handicap

The inability to perform at a satisfactory level all of the essential requirements of an occupation.

B.   Employment Handicap

The difficulty a disabled person may have in getting a suitable job because of discrimination (when there is no occupational handicap).

C.   Placement Handicap

When the rehabilitation worker has difficulty in placing a client on a job because of the client's occupational handicap, employment handicap, or both.

D.   Employability

Possessing the skills, abilities, and the worker traits necessary to perform a job.

E.   Placeability

Ability to actually find employment.

F.   Job Readiness

Preparation of physical, mental, emotional, and other vocational resources for entry into competitive employment.

G.   Work Tolerance

1.   Ability to sustain a work effort for a prolonged period of time.

2.   To maintain a steady flow of production at an acceptable pace and level of quality.

3.   To handle work pressure.

        4.   To fulfill all of the above without acting in an unsatisfactory manner or quitting.

H.   Job Club

        1.   Job-ready clients brought together as a group. Highly organized and structured approach to finding employment.

        2.   Job Club formulated by Nathan Azrin.

        3.   Based in behaviorism.

        4.   Utilizes peer reinforcement.

I.   Disability (See ADA for alternative definition)

A medically described disease or disorder (e.g. paraplegia, schizophrenia).

J.   Functional Limitation

A limitation in function which results from the disability (e.g. mobility, sensory, cognitive, behavior, motivity, etc.). See list last page of Part 6.

K.   Handicap

The ultimate effect(s) of the disability on the ability to work. (e.g. not being able to climb stairs to get to work. Or, the loss of a finger for a construction worker is not as much of a handicap as it is for someone who plays a piano.)

L.   Skills

Learned or acquired tasks which can be observed and measured.

M.   Transferability of Work Skills

Work behaviors which are learned by doing (e.g., typing) which may be usable in more than one occupation.

N.   Selective Job Placement

The special process of matching the requirements of a specified job with the relevant characteristics of the client in order to achieve compatibility.

O.   Situational Assessments

Based on the concept of the rehabilitation workshop. Rather than addressing specific work samples, this involves simulating the entire work environment (work activities, supervision, wages, time demands).

P.   Vocational Evaluation

1.   Predicts whether an individual will be both a satisfactory and satisfied worker.

2.   Exposes the individual to a variety of practical, realistic work activities that require an active response to the tools, tasks, and procedures employed in each work situation.

3.   Using data obtained during the evaluation, the evaluator draws conclusions regarding a person's vocational performance potential.

4.   Variables to consider in vocational evaluation are not only those dealing with stable characteristics or traits, but also the motivational or "choice-making" state of the person.

5.   **Motivation is a central variable in assessing work readiness to engage in the career exploration process.

XIII.   The Rehabilitation Team

A.   Medical Doctors

Addictionologist
        Addictions
Rheumatology
        Arthritis
Hematology
        Blood
Vascular Surgeon
        Blood Vessels
Orthopedist
        Muscles and Joints
Neoplastic/Oncology
        Cancer
Thoracic Surgeon
        Chest

Obstetrics

    Childbirth

Gastroenterologist

    Digestive

Otorhinolaryngologist

    Ear, Nose & Throat

Otolaryngologist

    Ears & Throat

Gerontologist

    Elder Care

Ophthalmologist

    Eyes

Podiatrist

    Feet

Gynecologist

    Female Health

Endocrinologist

    Glands

Epidemiologist

    Study of diseases

Cardiologist

    Heart

Neonatologist

    Infants

Pediatrician

    Children

Nephrologist

    Kidneys

Pulmonologist

    Lungs & Respiratory

Psychiatrist

> Emotional Disorders

Neurologist

> Nervous System Disorders (Parkinson's, seizures, etc.)

Neurosurgeon

> Nerve surgeon (brain, spinal cord, etc.)

Bariatric

> Obesity

Dermatologist

> Skin

Radiologist

> X-rays, MRI, CT Scans

Pathologist

> Disease Evaluation

Medical Examiner

> Forensic (e.g., cause of death for murder)

Anesthesiologist

> Pain Block

Physiatrist

> Physical Medicine and Rehabilitation

Urologist

> Urinary Tract

Proctologist

> Anal, rectum

B.   Physical Therapist

Carries out a physical restoration program to help alleviate disability and pain. Programs consist of exercises to develop strength, muscle reeducation, and increased range of motion.

C.   Occupational Therapist

Develops skills that will be useful in performing activities of daily living (ADLs). May also offer assistive technology services and upper extremity orthotics.

D.   Recreation Therapist

Plans and directs recreational activities for individuals recovering from physical and/or mental illness, or coping with disability.

E.   Vocational Counselor

Assists client in pursuit of vocation goals.

F.   Prosthetist

Creates artificial limbs/portions of the body.

G.   Rehabilitation Engineer

Applies principles of engineering to human biology and medicine.

H.   Speech/Language Pathologist and Audiologist

Provides diagnostic and rehabilitative services for individuals with various organic and functional speech and hearing disorders. Both typically belong to the same national association (American Speech and Hearing Association) although the audiologist specializes in hearing/deafness and the speech pathologist treats communications disorders. Some speech pathologists specialize in assistive technology. Others are experts in assessing neurological function with a focus on communication (e.g., brain injury).

XIV. Ramps

According to the American National Standard Institute (ANSI or ADA):

Width of ramps:
- An accessible route must be wide enough (36") for at least one wheelchair and should be wide enough for a walking person also (48").
- If the route is only the minimum width, then passing places for two wheelchairs (60") should be provided.

Slope of ramps:
- The accessible route should not rise more than one foot for every 12 feet of length.

XV.   Work incentive programs

1. Work Opportunity Tax Credit

- Federal government supported

- Deduct up to 40% of the first $6,000 of wages

- Can not exceed $2,500 tax reduction

- Must work 400 hours to receive full credit.

- Available to AFDC, SSI, food stamps, veterans, ex-felons, high risk youth.

- Must be certified by state

2. Ticket to Work and Work Incentives Improvement Act of 1999

- TWWIIA was enacted December 17, 1999.

- Two sections:

  o Improved access to employment training and placement services for people with disabilities.

  o Provides provision for work without fear of losing Medicare and Medicaid coverage. Government can charge for premiums part or fully depending on income.

- Administered by Social Security. (800/772-1213, www.ssa.gov/work) for SSI/SSDI

- Ages 18-65

- Vocational rehabilitation, job search assistance, job training, resume writing, job coaching, and more.

- TWWIIA Purposes

  - The Act has four purposes [Section 2(b) of the Act]:

    1. To provide health care and employment preparation and placement services to individuals with disabilities that will enable those individuals to reduce their dependency on cash benefit programs.

    2. To encourage states to adopt the option of allowing individuals with disabilities to purchase Medicaid coverage that is necessary to enable such individuals to maintain employment.

    3. To provide individuals with disabilities the option of maintaining Medicare coverage while working.

    4. To establish a return to work ticket program that will allow individuals with disabilities to seek the services necessary to obtain and retain employment and reduce their dependency on cash benefit programs.

- How rehabilitation counselors are paid.

  - The <u>outcome payment</u> system provides payment to employment networks up to 40% of the average monthly disability benefit payable for all beneficiaries for each month benefits are not payable to the beneficiary due to work, not to exceed 60 months. [Section 1148(h)(2) of the Social Security Act]

  - The <u>outcome-milestone payment</u> system is similar to the outcome payment system, except it provides for early payment(s) based on the achievement of one or more milestones directed towards the goal of permanent employment. To ensure the cost-effectiveness of the Program, the total amount must be less than the total amount that would have been payable under the outcome payment system.

3. Projects With Industry (PWI).

A discretionary grant program administered by the Rehabilitation Services Administration (RSA) of the U.S. Department of Education, and provides support assist individuals with disabilities to obtain competitive employment. Originally established by the 1968 amendments to the Rehabilitation Act, the PWI program was created to serve as a vehicle for promoting greater participation of business and industry in the vocational rehabilitation (VR) process.

Purposes of the PWI program are to:

1. Create and expand job and career opportunities for individuals with disabilities in the competitive labor market by engaging the talent and leadership of private industry as partners in the rehabilitation process;

2. Identify competitive job and career opportunities and the skills needed to perform these jobs;

3. Create practical settings for job readiness and job training programs; and

4. Provide job placements and career advancements.

XVI. Centers for Independent Living (See Part 1 for legislative authority)

A.   Goals

1.   Live as independently as possible

2.   Exercise as much control over life as possible

3.   Minimize reliance on others

4.   Minimize dependence on agencies and institutions

B.   Common Topics

1. Transportation and mobility

2. Communications

3. Self-care and appearance

4. Socialization

5. Functional reading and computation

6. Domestic behaviors

7. Health-care behaviors

C.   Four services typically offered

1. Information and referral--Centers maintain comprehensive information files on availability in their communities of accessible housing; transportation; employment opportunities; rosters of persons available to serve as personal care attendants, interpreters for hearing impaired people, or readers for visually impaired people; and many other services.

2. Independent living skills training--Centers provide training courses to help people with disabilities gain skills that would enable them to live more independently. Courses may include using various public transportation systems, managing a personal budget, dealing with insensitive and discriminatory behavior by members of the general public, and many other subjects.

3. Peer counseling--Centers offer a service in which a person with a disability can work with other persons who have disabilities and who are living independently in the community. The objective is to explore options and to solve problems that sometimes occur for people with disabilities, for example, making adjustments to a newly acquired disability, experiencing changes in living arrangements, or learning to use community services more effectively.

4. Advocacy--Centers provide two kinds of advocacy: (1) consumer advocacy, which involves center staff working with persons with disabilities to obtain necessary support services from other agencies in the community; and (2) community advocacy, which involves center staff, board members, and volunteers initiating activities to make changes in the community that make it easier for all persons with disabilities to live more independently.

D.   Funding

Typically under the U.S. Department of Education, funds are distributed through the Office of Special Education and Rehabilitation Services (OSERS), then through the Rehabilitation Services Administration (RSA). The funds are divided into 2 parts.

- Part B = Statewide Independent Living Councils (SILC).

- Part C = Centers for Independent Living (CIL)

XVII. Transition Programs

Transition planning services are available to special education students with severe disabilities who need to plan for a smooth transition from school to employment. This program is a cooperative effort with rehabilitation services, special education programs, employers, adult service agencies, community rehabilitation programs, and residential organizations.

Through this program, rehabilitation counseling, information, and referral to community services are available for special education students who typically are at least 16 years old.

During the transition planning process, students and their parents have the opportunity to discuss such topics as:

- Goals, priorities and preferences for life after school

- Residential, employment and support programs

- Application procedures, eligibility criteria or waiting lists for needed services

- Information about community resources and assistive technology

- Information about the Individual Education Plan (IEP) process, and the statement of needed transition services which is a required part of the IEP

- Advocacy

Source: http://www.srskansas.org/rehab/text/Transition.htm

XVIII. Life Care Planning

Life care planning is now a required knowledge area for CORE and presumably will appear on the CRC exam. Essentially the life care plan is a comprehensive plan for life long medical and non-medical care. Topics include:
- Future medical care
- Wheelchair needs (including accessories and maintenance)
- Prosthetic (artificial limbs) and orthotic (braces) products
- Assistive technology
- Leisure time activities
- Transportation (e.g. accessible van or hand controls)
- Architectural requirements (e.g., barrier free home, or specialized disability related additions)
- Durable medical equipment including hospital beds, mechanical standers, etc.)
- Medications

- Supplies
- Vocational related needs, etc.

The uninformed often portray that life care plans are only used in litigation (forensic rehabilitation). However, life care planning is appropriate for workers' compensation, estate planning, elder care, health maintenance organizations, and many other venues.

The definition is:

A Life Care Plan is a dynamic document based upon published standards of practice, comprehensive assessment, data analysis and research, which provides an organized concise plan for current and future needs with associated costs, for individuals who have experienced catastrophic injury or have chronic health care needs.

Source: Weed. R (Ed.) (2004). *Life Care Planning and Case Management Handbook* (2nd ed.). Boca Raton, FL: St. Lucie/CRC Press.

A.   Trait Factor Theory (Parsons, Williamson) (a person-environment "fit" theory)

    1.   People have different traits; each occupation demands a particular combination of characteristics in workers; vocational guidance should match people and jobs.

        a.   Study person

        b.   Study occupations

        c.   Match worker and occupation

    2.   Development of psychological tests to measure human traits.

    3.   Testing is a direct way to predict success in a job.

    4.   Basic framework for application of psychometric assessment.

B.   Need-Drive Theory (Maslow, Allport)

    1.   People make occupational decisions on the basis of their needs.

    2.   Individuals have needs that become the force or drive toward need-satisfying objects, individuals, or activities.

    3.   Work is a way of satisfying needs.

C.   Psychoanalytic Theory (Brill)

    1.   Occupational choice is based on sublimation and identification.

        a.   In sublimation, socially unacceptable motives are expressed as socially acceptable behavior (e.g., a person with extreme aggression becomes a boxer). Occupations are selected as general or specific sublimations of fundamental instinctual wishes or needs.

57

b.   In identification, a young person may transform his/her relationship with a parent into a model that directs vocational striving. Also, a powerful feeling of affinity with another person or group, which sometimes involves regarding somebody as a model and adopting his or her beliefs, values, or other characteristics

D.   Theory of Early Parent-Child Relationships (Anne Roe)

    1.   There are three essentially different psychological climates that result from early parent-child relationships.

        a.   Emotional concentration on the child results in an overprotective or over demanding climate.

        b.   Avoidance of the child results in a neglecting or rejecting climate.

        c.   Acceptance of the child results in a casual or loving climate.

    2.   There is a direct causal relationship between the childhood psychological climate and the evolution of the individual's needs hierarchy.

        a.   Warm parent-child relations result in children learning to satisfy their needs primarily through interaction with other people. They choose person-oriented occupations.

        b.   In cold modes of child-rearing, children learn to fulfill needs in ways that do not involve people (technology, outdoor, or ideas).

E.   Composite View (Hoppock)

    1.   Occupations meet needs.

    2.   Information about oneself influences occupational choice.

3. Information about occupations affects choices.

4. Job satisfaction depends upon the extent to which the job meets the needs one believes it should meet.

5. It is always appropriate to change occupational choice when one believes that a change will meet needs better.

F. General Theory (Axelrod, Ginzberg, Herma)

1. Ginzberg had the first developmental theory of occupational choice.

2. Occupational choice is a long term process. It becomes progressively irreversible; the final choice is a compromise between the person's ideal and the available realistic alternatives; the entire process takes place in a series of rather definitive stages or periods.

3. Selecting an occupation is a compromise in that when a choice is made, many possible decisions are eliminated.

G. Theory of Personality and Model Environments (John Holland)

1. Stresses the determinants of occupational choice.

    a. At the time of vocational choice, a person is the product of the interaction of heredity with a variety of cultural and personal forces (significant others, physical environment).

    b. Out of this, the person develops a hierarchy of preferred methods for dealing with environmental tasks.

    c. The person making a vocational choice searches for work situations which satisfy his or her hierarchy of adjustive orientations.

    d. Almost all well known interest inventories, the O*Net, and Richard Bolles' book, What Color is Your Parachute, use Holland Themes as basis for interest factors.

2.   Themes: Realistic, Investigative, Social, Enterprising, Conventional, and Artistic

Realistic (R)

- Usually has mechanical and athletic abilities, and likes to work outdoors and with tools and machines.
- Generally likes to work with things more than with people.
- Described as conforming, frank, genuine, hardheaded, honest, humble, materialistic, modest, natural, normal, persistent, practical, shy, and thrifty.
- Examples: auto mechanic, aircraft controller, surveyor, electrician, and farmer.

Investigative (I)

- Usually has math and science abilities, and likes to work alone and to solve problems.
- Generally likes to explore and understand things or events, rather than persuade others or sell them things.
- Is described as analytical, cautious, complex, critical, curious, independent, intellectual, introverted, methodical, modest, pessimistic, precise, rational, and reserved.
- Examples: biologist, chemist, physicist, geologist, anthropologist, laboratory assistant, and medical technician.

Artistic (A)

- Usually has artistic skills, enjoys creating original work, and has a good imagination.
- Generally likes to work with creative ideas and self-expression more than routines and rules.

- Is described as complicated, disorderly, emotional, expressive, idealistic, imaginative, impractical, impulsive, independent, introspective, intuitive, nonconforming, open, and original.
- Examples: composer, musician, stage director, dancer, interior decorator, actor, and writer.

Social (S)

- Usually likes to be around other people, is interested in how people get along, and likes to help other people with their problems.
- Generally likes to help, teach, and counsel people more than mechanical or technical activity.
- Is described as convincing, cooperative, friendly, generous, helpful, idealistic, kind, patient, responsible, social, sympathetic, tactful, understanding, and warm.
- Examples: teacher, speech therapist, religious worker, counselor, clinical psychologist, and nurse.

Enterprising (E)

- Usually has leadership and public speaking abilities, is interested in money and politics, and likes to influence people.
- Generally likes to persuade or direct others more than work on scientific or complicated topics.
- Is described as acquisitive, adventurous, agreeable, ambitious, attention-getting, domineering, energetic, extroverted, impulsive, optimistic, pleasure-seeking, popular, self-confident, and sociable
- Examples: buyer, sports promoter, television producer, business executive, salesperson, travel agent, supervisor, and manager.

Conventional (C)

- Generally likes to follow orderly routines and meet clear standards, avoiding work that does not have clear directions.

- Is described as conforming, conscientious, careful, efficient, inhibited, obedient, orderly, persistent, practical, thrifty, and unimaginative.

- Has clerical and math abilities, likes to work indoors and to organize things.

- Examples: bookkeeper, financial analyst, banker, tax expert, secretary, and radio dispatcher.

H.   The Process of Occupational Decision-Making and Adjustment (Tiedeman, O'Hara)

1.   Career development is a process in which the individual resolves a group of general psychosocial crises, occupational aspects of these crises, and a sequence of problems or decisions that lasts throughout life.

2.   Decision-Making sequence.

I.   Self-Concept Theory and Career Patterns (Super)

1.   The most comprehensive and generally accepted among contemporary theories of vocational development.

2.   Developmental stages.

3.   While everyone goes through the same basic stages, individuals differ in the type, sequence, and duration of work and work-related activities within each stage.

4.   Vocational development

Developing and implementing a self-concept within the occupational world.

5. A vocational self-concept is but one aspect of the whole self-concept.

J. Model of Vocational Behavior/Relevance to People with Disabilities (David Hershenson)

    1. Constructs:

        a. Physical and psychosocial background

        b. Work personality

        c. Work competencies

        d. Work choice

    2. Disabilities most directly affect work competencies, and adjustment to disability relates most directly to work personality.

    3. The extent of vocational adjustment to disability depends on the prior nature of these constructs and their interrelationships, how far into the individual's career development the onset of disability occurs, and its specific impact on each of the elements in this model.

K. Minnesota Theory of Work Adjustment (Dawis and Lofquist)

    1. Work adjustment

        a. When the individual's needs and abilities correspond with the work environment's reinforcers and demands.

        b. The outcome of the interaction between an individual and his or her work environment.

    2. Satisfactoriness

    How well an individual's abilities correspond with the ability requirements of the work environment.

    3. Satisfaction

How well the work reinforces the individual, or how satisfying the work is to the individual.

4.   Tenure

     a.   The amount of time an individual stays in a certain work environment.

     b.   The ultimate criterion of work-adjustment.

     c.   The longer a person remains in a given work environment, the more likely it is that an effective adjustment with this environment has been achieved.

L.   Theory of Moral Development and Cognitive Stages (Lawrence Kohlberg)

     a.   An individual progresses through a stage process consisting of three levels; each level is comprised of two stages for a total of six stages.

     b.   The primary concern at each stage is with the principle of justice. Kohlberg distinguishes between a "rule," which proscribes action, and a "principle," which affords "a guide for choosing among behaviors."

     c.   An individual progressing through each of the stages uses a different set of principles and a new sense of justice.

     d.   The progression from Stage One to Stage Six (which very few people actually reach) is best described as a steady movement outward from the self.

Stage 1: Obedience and Punishment

Stage 2: Individualism and Moral Reciprocity

Stage 3: Mutual Interpersonal Expectations, Relationships and Conformity

Stage 4. The Stage of Social System and Conscience Maintenance

Stage 5: Social Contract

Stage 6: Universal Ethical Principles

M.   Different Voice Model (emphasis on women) (Carol Gilligan)

     a.   Care Voice v. Justice Voice: Women's moral reasoning is in the "care voice" while men tend to reason in the "justice voice."

     b.   For women the perception of self is "tenaciously embedded in relationships with others.

     c.   This "care voice" leads to women resolving moral conflicts by way of three stages.

Stage 1: Orientation to individual survival. This stage focuses squarely and clearly on the self.

Stage 2: Goodness as self-sacrifice. The good is equated with caring for others.

Stage 3: Resolution of the conflict between selfishness and responsibility. When equilibrium is found between the expectations of conformity and caring in conventional notions of womanhood and individual needs.

I.   Intelligence and Neurological Testing

    A.   Wechsler Scales

        1.   Instrument of choice in the measurement of intelligence.

        2.   Yields three IQ scores:

            a.   Verbal IQ

            b.   Performance IQ

            c.   Full Scale IQ

        3.   Wechsler Scales include (check reference for current version):

            a.   Wechsler Adult Intelligence Scale (WAIS)

            b.   Wechsler Intelligence Scale for Children (WISC)

            c.   Wechsler Preschool and Primary Scale of Intelligence (WPPSI)

        4.   Mean = 100, Standard deviation = 15

    B.   Bender Gestalt Visual Motor Test

        1.   Screening for brain damage/neurological impairment.

        2.   Assesses the ability to copy fairly complex geometric figures.

        3.   Provides clues about attention to detail, approaches to organization, and visual motor function.

        4.   Can serve as a useful tool as part of a comprehensive psychological test battery but its use as an independent measure of current intellectual functioning is not recommended.

C.   Stanford-Binet Scales

    1.   "Verbally" loaded

    2.   Its true value may be in its historical importance as a significant beginning point in the measure of intelligence.

    3.   Historically used with persons with mental retardation.

    4.   Mean = 100, standard deviation = 16

D.   Halstead-Reitan

    1.   Best known evaluation for diagnosis of brain damage and effects on behavior and cognitive functioning.

E.   Luria-Nebraska

    1.   Second most well-known evaluation following the Halstead-Reitan for diagnosing brain damage.

    2.   Also known for helping to determine rehabilitation programs for persons with traumatic brain injury.

F.   Haptic

    1.   Provides a measure of intelligence for clients who have visual impairments.

    2.   Normed upon persons with visual impairments.

    3.   The verbal section of the Wechsler is also often used to test intelligence of persons with visual impairments.

G.   Leiter

    1.   Nonverbal scale for persons with hearing impairments, aphasia, or mental retardation.

    2.   Has been described as the "nonverbal Binet."

    3.   May help in the assessment of individuals with whom the Binet or WAIS-R is inappropriate.

H.   Hisky - Nebraska

Learning aptitude for deaf clients.

I.   Slosson Intelligence Test

    1.   An oral assessment of verbal intelligence.

    2.   Considered low power IQ test and is useful as a screening tool.

J.   Shipley Institute of Living Scale

    1.   Used to assess decline in intellectual functioning (e.g. due to the aging process).

    2.   Limited as a standard measure of intelligence.

K.   Raven's Progressive Matrices

    1.   Considered a test of reasoning but also used for IQ.

    2.   Is a visual test with progressively more detailed "puzzles" to solve

II.   Measures of Personality

A.   Minnesota Multiphasic Personality Inventory (MMPI)

1. Most frequently used inventory for the evaluation and diagnosis of clinical personality symptoms and disorders for adults.

   MMPI-A, for adolescents — ages 14-18.

2. Screening for psychiatric disturbance on the following 10 substantive scales:

   Hypochondriasis   (Hs)

   Paranoia   (Pa)

   Psychasthenia   (Pt)

   Schizophrenia   (Sc)

   Depression   (D)

   Psychopathic Deviate   (Pd)

   Hypomania   (Ma)

   Masculinity-Femininity   (Mf)

   Hysteria   (Hy)

   Social Introversion   (Si)

3. Validity scales include:

   L (lie) Scale – includes items that are common human faults that most people are willing to admit; thus if the person does not admit to these faults he or she is likely to be exaggerating his or her virtues by claiming they possess unrealistically high moral standards.

   F (infrequency) Scale – includes items that ask questions to determine any inconsistency where the client has contradicted themselves in there responses.

   K (correction) Scale – includes items which are designed to reveal the client's attempts to present themselves in the best possible way.

   Sometimes the "? (cannot say) Scale" is added –? is the number of items that the client has left unanswered and reported as a raw score.

4. Useful tool in assessing personality factors related to vocational needs and in understanding the long-time psychological adjustment of rehabilitation clients.

5. National norms on persons with mental disabilities.

B. 16 Personality Factor Questionnaire (16PF)

1. Most extensively studied and widely used device for assessing personality

2. Features 16 primary personality characteristics:

Warmth	Impulsivity
Suspiciousness	Intelligence
Conformity	Imagination
Emotional stability	Boldness
Shrewdness	Dominance
Sensitivity	Insecurity
Self-sufficiency	Radicalism
Self-discipline	Tension

3. Computer-generated interpretation termed the Personal Career Development Profile. It is based on patterns important to vocational exploration:

Testing orientation

Problem solving

Coping with stressful conditions

Interpersonal interactions

Organizational role and work setting

Career activity interests

Personal career life-style considerations

Occupational comparisons

4.   Weak in assessing major affective and cognitive disorders

5.   Form E of the 16 PF has reduced reading level and is normed on rehabilitation clients.

C.   Myers-Briggs Type Indicator (MBTI)

1.   Provides a measure of Carl Jung's theory of psychological types.

2.   Accentuates positive aspects of personality.

3.   Individuals are classified as one of two preferences from four dimensions:

Extraverted	(E)	or	Introverted	(I)
Sensing	(S)	or	Intuiting	(N)
Thinking	(T)	or	Feeling	(F)
Judging	(J)	or	Perceiving	(P)

D.   Rorschach

1.   A projective technique used for psychological evaluation and personality appraisal.

2.   The client is presented with 10 inkblots one at a time and is asked to describe what the images look like or what they see.

3.   Interpretation is subjective, complex, and formal.

E.   Thematic Apperception Test (TAT)

1.   A projective technique used for psychological evaluation and personality appraisal.

2. Consists of 31 pictures designed to represent major life situations.

3. Respondents are instructed to "tell a story" describing the picture and include what the characters are doing, feeling, and thinking, what they have done in the past, and what they may do in the future, then indicate an ending.

4. Pictures are out of date and often not applicable to persons with disabilities.

F. Draw-A-Person Test

1. A projective technique used to describe personality characteristics.

2. Yields rich information on self-concept, personality style, and conflict areas.

3. The client is provided with paper and pencil and asked to draw a human figure.

4. Most assessors ask for stories about the person drawn.

5. Scoring may take into account such signs as figure size, figure placement, pencil pressure, shading, and body parts or omissions.

III. Interest Testing

A. Strong Interest Inventory (SCII)

1. Gives individuals, in 8th grade to adult, information about themselves and their preferences for activities that will help them to make sound career decisions.

2. Measures occupational interests in professional, technical, non-professional, and vocational-technical areas.

3. Provides an index of similarity between a person's interests and those of successful individuals in a wide range of occupations.

4. Provides information about the world of work.

5. Promotes occupational exploration by assessing an individual's pattern of interests.

6. Most items are answered in a like, dislike, or indifferent format and are grouped into the following categories:

Occupations	Types of People
School Subjects	Activities
Preference for activities	Your characteristics
(choose between two)	(answer with yes, no, or ?)

7. Four major sections in the profile:

   a. General Occupational Themes (based on the Holland Typology)

   b. Basic Interest Scales

   c. Occupational Scales

   d. Special Scales

      (1) Academic comfort

      (2) Introversion-Extroversion

B. Self-Directed Search (SDS)

   1. Provides vocational counseling for individuals not needing or having direct access to career counseling services.

   2. Minimal counselor involvement is needed; therefore, can facilitate services to more clients.

   3. Based on the Holland theory of personality types and work environments:

There are six types based on Holland's theory of personality orientations and environmental models: (Note: most interest inventories, including the O*Net, use the Holland typologies below).

   Realistic (R): Practical, robust, work with hands

Investigative (I): Scientific, work independently, think things through

Artistic (A): Free, unstructured, creative, intuitive, musical, poetry

Social (S): Humanistic, religious interests, avoid intellectual problem solving, social work

Enterprising (E): Persuasive, leaders, selling, enjoy power/status

Conventional (C): Well ordered environments, clerical, office work, efficient, orderly, accounting

Individuals are more likely to experience job satisfaction if the work environment matches their personalities.

4. SDS, Form E (Easy) developed for limited readers or for individuals with educational levels below the ninth grade.

5. Contains a wide variety of occupational choices.

C. Enhanced Career Assessment Inventory (CAI)

1. Used in career exploration and career decision-making.

2. Geared toward clients who are seeking to enter the labor force or non-college training.

3. Orientation is to non-professional jobs.

4. For purposes of interpretation, there are three general scales based on the Holland Occupational Themes (General Theme, Basic Interest, and Occupation).

5. Useful for clients for whom either direct placement or short-term training are considerations.

6. Asks questions related to activities, school subjects, and occupational titles. Each question has five responses ranging from "very much like" to "very much dislike."

7. Also measures occupational extraversion and introversion, and variability of interests.

D.   Kuder Occupational Interest Survey (KOIS)

1.   Useful for high school students, dropouts, college freshmen, and adults in need of career planning or job placement services.

2.   Measures preferences, likes, and dislikes for activities, and compares them with those of persons in a wide range of occupations.

3.   Used to assist in vocational exploration and vocational decision-making.

4.   Can be helpful in narrowing or widening career alternatives.

E.   Minnesota Importance Questionnaire (MIQ)

1.   Assesses vocational needs and values of clients.

2.   Helps clients assess the correspondence between their needs and reinforcer patterns in various occupations.

a.   Need reinforcer correspondence in a particular occupation indicates the likelihood that a client will be satisfied in that occupation.

3.   Helps individuals identify their psychological needs as manifested in a work setting.

4.   Clients are asked to choose the one in a pair of statements that they feel is more important to them in their ideal job.

5.   Unlike the Strong-Campbell and the Kuder, the Minnesota Importance Questionnaire does not compare an individual's scores with a normative group to obtain a scale score.

F.   Salience Inventory (SI)

1.   A measure of work values.

2.   Assesses the relative importance of the following 5 major life roles in individuals and cultures:

Study   Home

Work   Leisure

Community

G.   Reading-Free Vocational Interest Inventory

1.   Designed to assess, in a forced-choice format, the vocational preferences of clients with limited reading ability.

2.   Provides information about vocational interests for persons with Mental Retardation and Learning Disabilities through the use of pictures of individuals engaged in various occupational tasks.

3.   Contains 55 triads of illustrations. Each illustration depicts an individual engaged in a task typical of an unskilled, semi-skilled, or skilled occupation. Clients are instructed to select the picture they would most like to do.

4.   Illustrations depict the following fields that this population realistically can be assumed to succeed in:

Automotive   Patient Care

Building trades   Horticulture

Clerical   Housekeeping

Animal care   Personal service

Food service   Laundry service

Materials handling

H.   Geist Picture Interest Inventory

1.   A pictorially-oriented interest inventory for persons who lack the reading levels needed for the Kuder or Strong-Campbell.

2.   Useful for non-verbal/non-expressive clients because it may stimulate client participation in the counseling process.

3.   Careful observation by the counselor can enhance understanding of the client's needs and thought processes.

I.   My Vocational Situation (MVS)

1.   Career development and maturity instrument as opposed to interest inventory.

2.   Very brief 2-page questionnaire that determines which of the following possibilities may be preventing a client from making a career decision:

a.   Lack of vocational identity.

b.   Lack of information or training.

c.   Environmental or personal barriers.

3.   More research and refining is still needed.

IV.   Aptitude Batteries

A.   General Aptitude Test Battery (GATB) (Rarely used due to predictive validity research. However, the privately produced Apticom is based on the GATB – see below). The results fit with the transferability worksheet (aka VDARE).

The U. S. Employment Service (USES) Testing Program

1.   Measures vocational aptitudes of clients aged 16 and older.

2.   Unsurpassed as a vocational aptitude battery.

3.   Measures 9 aptitudes:

Intelligence   (G)

Verbal Aptitude   (V)*

Numerical Aptitude   (N)*

Spatial Aptitude   (S)*

Form Perception   (P)

Clerical Perception   (Q)

Motor Coordination   (K)

Finger Dexterity   (F)

Manual Dexterity   (M)

* These (V, S, N) three scores combined yield (G) Intelligence score

4. Occupational Aptitude Patterns (OAPs)

    a. A pattern of scores that identifies one or more Work Groups for which the individual is suited.

    b. Combinations of GATB aptitudes with associated cut-off scores.

    c. Indicates aptitude requirements for occupations.

    d. Covers 97% of non-supervisory occupations in the DOT.

    e. Relates directly to the Guide for Occupational Exploration.

5. Specific Aptitude Test Batteries (SATBs)

    a. Combinations of aptitudes with associated cut-off scores for specific occupations.

    b. Used in predicting whether or not an individual is likely to be successful in specific occupations.

6. Mean = 100, Standard deviation = 20

B. Nonreading Aptitude Test Battery (NATB)

1. Developed by the U.S. Employment Service (USES).

    2.   Measures the same aptitudes as the GATB for disadvantaged or semi-literate adults and individuals in grades 9-12.

C.   Apticom™ (modeled after government's GATB)

    1.   Combined assessment program.

    2.   Provides a quick vocational assessment in aptitudes, interests, and educational level, and combines them into job recommendations.

    3.   Measures U.S. Department of Labor aptitudes, the Guide for Occupational Exploration interests, and language and math skills.

    4.   Designed for English or Spanish speaking disadvantaged job applicants, high school or special education students, and rehabilitation clients.

    5.   The major device is a plastic pegboard approximately 2' X 2', containing holes that correspond to test answers. Test items are contained on plastic overlays that are placed on the board.

    6.   The Apticom is highly speeded but reportedly has better reliability than many other USES tests.

    7.   Currently available on computer, which provides instant results/report.

D.   Armed Services Vocational Aptitude Battery (ASVAB)

    1.   Devised by the U.S. Department of Defense (DOD) to provide military service recruiters with test score information on secondary and post-secondary students.

    2.   Now designed for all youths ages 16 - 23. Is given through the schools and the Department of Defense. The DOD maintains direct supervision of the ASVAB.

E. Differential Aptitude Tests (DAT)

    1. Aptitude tests designed for educational and vocational guidance in grades 8 through 12 and adults. The following aptitudes are measured:

        a. Verbal reasoning

        b. Spelling

        c. Language usage

        d. Numerical ability

        e. Clerical speed and accuracy

        f. Abstract reasoning

        g. Spatial relations

        h. Mechanical reasoning

    2. A career planning program can be ordered in addition to the above tests.

F. McCarron-Dial (MDS)

    1. Vocational and clinical evaluation.

    2. Originally normed on people with mental retardation. Currently also used with neurological (e.g., acquired brain injury) impairments as well. Can be used with special education and rehabilitation populations at any level of intellectual functioning and with physical, mental, or emotional disabilities.

    3. Assesses the following 5 traits:

        a. Motor

        b. Emotional

        c. Verbal, spatial, cognitive

        d. Sensory

        e.   Integration/coping

V.   Measurements of Work Readiness

    A.   Work Adjustment Rating Form (WARF)

        1.   An objective measure of job readiness used with clients with mental retardation in workshops by counselors and supervisors.

        2.   Contains 8 subscales with five items each. The items describe five different levels of performance from high to low with rater judgments made on a yes-no basis. The scales include:

           a.   Amount of supervision required

           b.   Realism of job goals

           c.   Teamwork

           d.   Acceptance of rules and authority

           e.   Work tolerance

           f.   Perseverance in work

           g.   Extent to which client seeks assistance

           h.   Importance attached to job training

    B.   Vocational Behavior Checklist (VBC)

        1.   Contains 339 vocationally relevant skill objectives presented in terms of conditions, behaviors, and standards of performance.

        2.   Client skill mastery is recorded and translated into a percentage of the critical behaviors mastered in each of 7 content areas.

    C.   Work Samples
        A <u>work sample</u> is a well-defined work-activity involving tasks, materials, and tools that have been identified as similar to those in an actual job or cluster of jobs.

Work samples were developed to supplement or replace other ability and aptitude measures that either could not be used with persons with disabilities or were difficult to use with individuals who did not readily relate to pencil and paper tests. The advantage of work samples is realism. Experience with individuals with severe disabilities indicates a need to modify the approach to assessment from reliance on standardized work samples to more individualized approaches. Two examples of work samples are the following:

Valpar

1. A series of work samples, physical functioning and aptitude tests relevant to vocational placement.

2. For special populations including work injured, learning disabled, and people with mental retardation, ranging from junior high school students through adulthood.

3. Scores on the test are not as important as interpreting observations made during the observation.

D. TOWER

1. The oldest commercial vocational evaluation system.

2. Based on job analysis. Places the client in a realistic job setting.

3. Includes tasks such as clerical, drafting, and electronics assembly that have face validity for the person being tested.

**The Valpar and TOWER are both work samples named for their manufacturers.

VI. Assessment of Physical Functioning

A. Barthel Inventory of Self-Care Skills and Mobility Skills

1. One of the most widely used measures of physical functioning in medical rehabilitation.

2.	Very brief.

3.	9 self-care and 6 mobility items.

4.	Patient indicates whether it is possible to do the task alone, with someone's help, or not at all.

5.	An instrument designed to indicate client independence in mobility and activities of daily living.

B.	PULSES Scale of Severity of Disability

1.	Four point rating scale in six broad areas of disability. The areas include:

P - Physical condition

U - Upper limb functions especially self-care

L - Lower limb functions especially mobility

S - Sensory component including sight and communication

E - Excretory functions

S - Support factors including psychological, family, social, and financial

2.	Scores range from 6 (indicating little or no disability) to 24. A score of 12 = the cutoff for relatively severe disability and a score of 16 = very severely disabled.

C.	Vineland Social Maturity Scale

1.	Excellent measure of adaptive behavior.

2.	Suitable for use with non-institutionalized individuals with mental retardation.

VII.   Achievement Tests

A.   Wide Range Achievement Test (WRAT)

1.   Screening device for approximate educational level.

2.   Constructs scored include (1) reading (word recognition), (2) spelling, and (3) arithmetic.

3.   Consists of Level 1 and Level 2. Level I used for persons with lower intellect. Useful for most age and educational levels.

B.   Peabody Individual Achievement Test (PIAT)

1.   Quick measure of educational level.

2.   Constructs scored include reading, reading comprehension, spelling, mathematics, and general information.

3.   Unlike the Wide Range Achievement Test - Revised, the Peabody Individual Achievement Test also offers a score for reading comprehension.

C.   Woodcock Johnson Psychoeducational Battery (WJ)

1.   Primarily used with clients who have learning disabilities.

2.   Two batteries (a) cognitive ability and (b) academic achievement.

3.   One of the few tests that meets the requirements to label student as learning disabled in public schools.

D.   Tests of General Educational Development (GED)

1.   Designed to test candidates for high school equivalency certificates.

2.   Constructs scored include interpretation of reading materials in the social sciences, natural sciences, and correctness and effectiveness of expression.

E.   Basic Occupational Literacy Test (BOLT)

    1.   A test of basic reading (literacy) and arithmetic skills for use with educationally deficient adults.

    2.   Provides scores for reading vocabulary, reading comprehension, arithmetic computation, and arithmetic reasoning.

    3.   Yields 3 general educational development (G.E.D.) levels.

I.   Levels of Measurement (with "quick references" in parentheses)

   A.   Nominal Scale (numbers as labels only, but these labels do not
            have additional meaning)

   Uses numbers as labels to identify subjects (e.g. females assigned a score of 1,
   males assigned a score of 2 but one is not better than the other).

   B.   Ordinal Scale (order and rank)

   Used when people in a group are to be placed in rank order on a measured
   attribute (e.g. 1st, 2nd, and 3rd place in a race but there is no known
   magnitude of difference between each).

   C.   Interval Scale

   An ordinal scale with an established unit of measurement, but with no zero
   point. This scale makes it possible to estimate the magnitude of differences
   between individuals, in addition to knowing simply that one possesses more
   (or less) of a trait than another person (e.g. Fahrenheit scale- zero does not
   mean there is no temperature).

   D.   Ratio Scale

   This indicates the properties of an interval scale, and also has a zero point
   (e.g. height and weight).

   *Most psychological tests are based on ordinal and interval scales.

II.   Standard scores in the Normal Distribution (Also known as the Bell Curve or
Gaussian Curve – see next page)

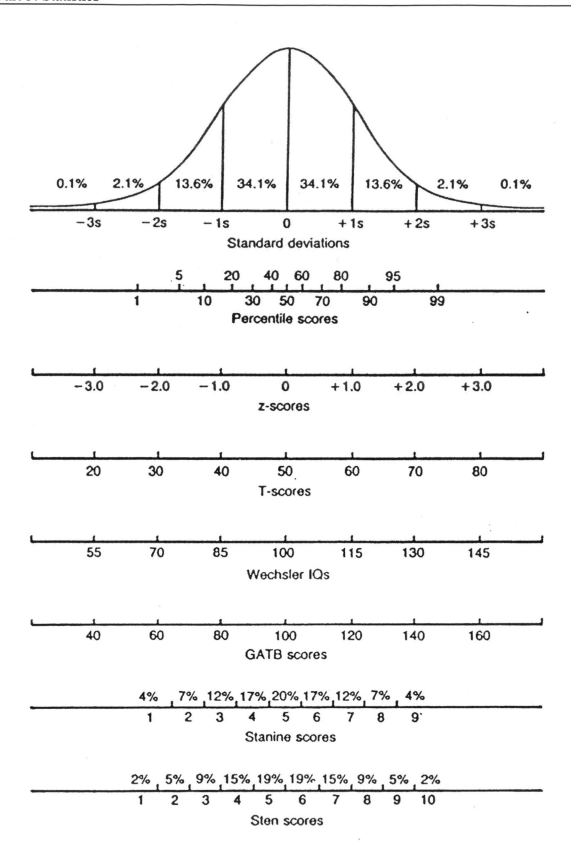

III.   Reliability

The extent to which a measuring device is <u>consistent</u> in whatever it measures.

    A.   Test - Retest Reliability

        Administer a test twice to the same group of individuals and correlate the paired scores (e.g. Administer 1st test in May and 2nd in December).

    B.   Equivalent (or Alternate or Parallel) Forms Reliability

        Equivalent forms of the test are administered to the same individuals; scores are correlated. This is used when it is probable that subjects will remember their responses to the first form of the test.

    C.   Internal Consistency Measures of Reliability

        This is designed to determine whether all the items on a test are measuring the same thing. This only requires a single administration of one form of a test.

    D.   Split Half Reliability

        Split the test into two halves and correlate the individual's scores on the two forms.

IV.   Validity

The extent to which an instrument measures what it is intended, or purports, to measure.

A.   Construct Validity

The degree to which the measure or test reflects the theoretical construct (e.g. intelligence) it was intended to reflect.

B.   Content Validity

How well the test items used to measure a skill (e.g. mathematics ability) actually reflect performance on the whole domain of behaviors that constitute that trait.

C.   Criterion-Related Validity

The extent to which a measure of a trait demonstrates an association with some independent or external measure of the same trait.

1.   Predictive Validity

How a present score on a test predicts future status on the criterion variable (e.g. SAT scores predicting college achievement).

2.   Concurrent Validity

Both the predictor and criterion scores are obtained at the same time; the relationship between present status on the test and present status on the criterion is studied (e.g. The MMPI assessing pathology).

D.   Face Validity

The extent to which an instrument appears to measure what it is intended to measure.

*A test can not be valid unless it is reliable.

**A test can be reliable without being valid.

***A test's validity score can not be higher than its reliability score.

V.   Measures of Central Tendency

    A.   Mean (average)

    Most widely used measure of central tendency. It is the sum of all the values in a distribution divided by the number of cases. Also known as the arithmetic average.

    B.   Median (middle)

    That point in a distribution of measures below which 50% of the cases lie and above which 50% of the cases will lie.

    C.   Mode (most often)

    That value in a distribution that occurs most frequently.

VI.   Measures of Variability

    A.   Range

    The difference between the highest and the lowest scores in a distribution. It is found by subtracting the smallest value from the highest.

B.   Standard Deviation

     1.   Uniform distance on the bell curve.

     2.   A measure of how variable the scores are.

C.   Standard Error of Measurement (SEM)

The true score for a test is subject to errors of measurement. This is expressed in scores which are plus or minus a certain number of points. For example, your I.Q. score may be 100 with a 3 point plus or minus SEM. This means that your true score is probably between 97 and 103.

VII.   Miscellaneous Statistical Terms

A.   Correlation

Indicates association (but not necessarily causation) between variables. The correlation coefficient(r) can range from -1 to +1 with the following guidelines:

$r = 0$ No association between variables

$r = +1$ Strong positive/direct relationship

$r = -1$ Strong negative/indirect relationship

B.   Individual vs. Group Administration

     1.   Individually administered tests allow opportunities for the examiner to use judgment in adapting to the disability of the examinee and to gather clinically relevant information during the testing session.

     2.   Group administered testing is more economical.

C. Research designs

1. Qualitative: Often case studies or research on individuals rather than comparisons of groups of subjects.

2. Quantitative: Often referred to as "hard data research." The use of statistics to attempt to determine variations within or among groups of subjects.

D. Internal and external validity

1. Internal validity is the basic minimum without which any experiment is uninterpretable (did the experimental treatment make a difference).

2. External validity refers to whether the results can be generalized.

3. Threats to Internal Validity include:

- History (did something happen between the first and second treatments that might account for the difference).

- Maturation (did the subject mature, grow older, become tired, become hungry, which might affect the results).

- Testing (did the effects of taking the test make a difference).

- Instrumentation (were there changes in the instruments or observers that may account for differences).

- Statistical regression (extreme scores commonly "regress toward the mean").

- Selection biases (is the sample representative or biased).

- Experimental mortality (did people drop out or move and cannot be located).

- Selection-maturation interaction

4. Threats to external validity include:

- Reactive or interaction effect of testing (the test instrument may be worded to influence the outcome).

- Interaction effects of selection biases and experimental variable.

- Reactive effect of experimental arrangements (where the effect of the variable being exposed to it in a non-experimental setting).

- Multiple-treatment interference (because prior treatments to the same individuals are not erasable).

E.   Research error

- Type I error occurs when the difference detected in the study is accepted as true when it is not.

- Type II error occurs when no difference is detected, but a difference actually does exist.

GENERAL INFORMATION

1. Fee for service (traditional)
   - Doctor or hospital of choice
   - File for reimbursement
   - Pays a portion of fees (80 % of "usual & customary")
   - Out of pocket expenses
   - Usually more expensive

2. Preferred Provider Organization (PPO)
   - A network plan where you use people in the network
   - Can also often pick MD off network but costs more
   - Larger network than HMOs
   - More expensive than HMO - but cheaper than fee for service

3. Point of Service Plan (POS)
   - Combines features of HMO and fee for service
   - Reduced freedom to choose MD
   - Can go outside of system, but costs more
   - Must see primary MD before specialist
   - Less expensive except for HMO

4. Health Maintenance Organization (HMO)
   - Prepaid health plan – Generally the cheapest
   - Small fees for visits or medicine
   - Reduced paperwork
   - Have to use providers in network
   - Generally good for "healthy"
   - Rehabilitation for serious injury usually limited
   - May be hard to see MD unless know system

ACQUIRED IMMUNODEFICIENCY SYNDROME (AIDS)

AIDS is a chronic viral infection from the human immunodeficiency virus (HIV) that produces severe, life threatening disease that reduces the body's ability to fight disease (autoimmune system). Usually fatal although "cocktail" medication treatment (AZT, ddI, ddC, and antibiotics) has been effective and some consider the disease to be "chronic" rather than fatal.

The disease spreads via sexual contact, sharing of contaminated drug needles, transfusions, especially prior to 1985, and through infected women passing the disease on to the fetus. Testing with ELISA or Western Blot test after approximately six months of suspected infection will reveal diagnosis.

Prevention is through sexual abstinence, no illicit drug use, and use of a latex condom. Heath caregivers have adopted "universal precautions," which include wearing gloves, mask, gown and ear wear. Also included are sterilization techniques and disposal of needles in a special container.

Vocational aspects include attitudinal barriers by employers and co-workers. The Americans with Disabilities Act (ADA) protects clients with AIDS and those who are *believed* to have AIDS. People with HIV can be symptom free for years. Once symptoms are experienced, the vocational counselor will need to carefully assess the individual's functional limitations. Common problems include multiple visits to the physician, diarrhea, cognitive impairments, fatigue, and psychological reactions. Working in food service with AIDS is *not* necessarily considered a direct threat under the ADA.

ALCOHOLISM

A chronic, progressive and potentially fatal disease characterized by tolerance, physical dependency and/or pathological organ changes all of which are direct or indirect consequences of alcohol ingested.

Functional Limitations

During drinking episodes, memory, judgment, and fine and gross motor coordination will be impaired. Activities of daily living are generally not limited, but during the first six months of recovery, tremors may affect writing ability, and there may be short-term memory lapses and inability to concentrate. Uninterrupted alcoholism over a long period of time can lead to brain damage, but in many cases this will be temporary if an individual can achieve and maintain abstinence.

Psychological Aspects

1.   Dependency - The counselor should always avoid doing things for the client that she/he can do for him or herself.

2.   Anxiety - Related to remaining sober, i.e. loss of the tension-reducing properties of alcohol, undergoing change.

3.   Isolation - If alcohol consumption is the alcoholic's most effective way of communicating with others and of relieving pain, then she/he generally does not trust people and is seemingly more concerned with getting something from them than in genuinely relating to them.

4.   Denial - For example, the alcoholic may convince him/herself that if she/he stops drinking, everything will be rectified, the pain inflicted and suffered will be healed, and life will automatically adjust to normal. (Oversimplification)

5.   Inaccurate Self-Appraisal - Overestimating abilities, having unrealistic goals.

6.   Impatience - Seeks immediate gratification, demanding (especially of counselor).

Vocational Aspects

Alcohol interfering with work is one indication of alcoholism. Vocational planning is dependent on sobriety and vocational and psychological testing should not take place until the person has fully recovered which could be as much as six months after detoxification. Entering a program designed to help the alcoholic maintain abstinence must be accomplished prior to job-seeking and/or retraining. Client should not overcome by working too many hours or days. Client should also not take on more responsibility than she/he can handle. Stress and anxiety are likely to increase whenever the client is going through change. Counselor should offer extra support during these times.

AMPUTATIONS

Loss of a body part due to

1. Congenital deficiencies
2. Vascular difficulty
3. Injury

Abbreviations

1.	S/D	Shoulder disarticulation (disarticulation = amputation at the joint)
2.	A/E	Above the elbow
3.	E/D	Elbow disarticulation
4.	B/E	Below the elbow
5.	W/D	Wrist disarticulation
6.	H/P	Hemipelvectomy
7.	H/D	Hip disarticulation
8.	A/K	Above the knee
9.	K/D	Knee disarticulation
10.	B/K	Below knee (BBK =bilateral below knee)
11.	Syme	Ankle

Complications

1. Phantom pain - Feeling of pain - which can be severe, even debilitating - in what was the amputated body part.

2. Phantom sensation - Feeling that the amputated body part is still present.

3. Edema (swelling) - Takes place immediately following amputation and in the course of prosthesis wear.

4. Ulceration - Occurs during prosthesis wear due to excess pressure or chronic edema.

5. Contractions - May occur as a result of efforts to save the limb over an extended period of time during which the extremity is inactive and treatment needs prevent full joint range of motion.

6. Scoliosis - Secondary to imbalance of trunk, unequal leg lengths, or insufficient use of prosthesis.

7. Infection - Occurs when ulceration gets contaminated, or through neglect of stump cleanliness.

8. Bone Overgrowth - Bone spurs may occur due to insufficient cutting of the bone at time of amputation. In young persons, bone may grow faster than the skin around the stump.

Special Notes

1. Stump care is essential.
2. Prosthesis fitting can only be done after stabilization of the stump.
3. Weight control is very important (increase/decrease of 10% = socket change).

Vocational Implications

For persons with upper extremity amputation, if work is intellectual in nature, few changes may be necessary. Persons involved with manual labor will have limitations, however, as eye-hand and finger-hand dexterity may be absent. Amputees should prepare for white-collar jobs.

Persons with lower extremity amputation might avoid very warm environments as they can cause sweating and result in skin problems on the stump. Cold, dust, and sand can injure the prosthetic components. Uneven ground should be avoided as should carrying objects. Amputees from burns may have additional skin problems and experience skin break down from prosthetic use. Weight gain or loss can cause premature re-fitting of prosthesis. Complicated or multiple amputations may require loss of work time due to medical care and maintenance of prostheses. Use of prosthesis requires more energy so fatigue can be a problem for physically demanding related employment.

AUTISM

Autistic Disorders require that five criteria be met.

(1) At least two aspects of social interaction must be deficient, such as lack of eye contact, inappropriate use of facial expression or body language, difficulties in developing and maintaining friendships, or failure to exhibit social reciprocity.

(2) There must be significant impairment in communication skills, as evidence by either a lack of spoken language or a delay in language development, inability to initiate or sustain conversations, a tendency to repeat certain words or phrases, or the lack of imaginative or imitative play.

(3) Specifies either the presence of an unusual pattern of interest, a rigid adherence to unusual routines, or repetitive patterns of unusual bodily movements.

(4) The symptoms must be apparent before three years of age.

Asperger's Syndrome shares two of the criteria required for Autistic Disorder, namely, marked deficits in social interaction and the presence of either restricted interests or stereotyped movements. Such impairments must seriously hinder social, occupational, or other types of functioning. In contrast to Autistic Disorder, however, persons with Asperger's Syndrome do not exhibit significant delays in language or cognitive development.

BLINDNESS AND VISUAL IMPAIRMENTS

Blindness is defined as anatomic and functional disturbances in visual ability sufficient to cause total loss of light perception. Those who are severely impaired - but do have some remaining visual function - are considered legally blind. One condition for legal blindness is less 20/200 with best correction or less than 20 degrees of field of vision. Vision impairment is another category usually associated with aging (macular degeneration and cataracts). However, other problems such as brain injury, diseases, and eye trauma can also cause vision impairment sufficient to impair vocational choice.

Occupations that are either intellectual in nature or involve manipulation of a tangible object may be preferred.

Employer and co-worker education is encouraged to dispel any myths they may have about blindness.

With proper counseling, aids, training, and job survey, it is estimated that 80% of the jobs in the DOT can be performed by legally blind or blind persons. Large print or "talking" computers, computer-based voice readers for printed documents are also available. The most popular computer program for text reading is JAWS (Job Access with Speech).

Professionals involved in eye care may include:

Ophthalmologist – a physician (MD or DO) who specializes in eye care and diseases.

Optometrist – OD (not DO) does not have MD degree but may diagnose and treat eyes as well as prescribe low vision devices and lenses.

Rehabilitation Teacher – Primarily work with the blind in their homes teaching self care, home maintenance care and activities of daily living (ADLs).

Orientation and Mobility Instructor – Teaches the blind to find their way around, teaches to listen for environmental cues and use existing transportation. May also teach Braille.

Sighted Guide – An individual that accompanies the blind person when needed (skiing, conferences, others unfamiliar public places, etc.).

People with both vision and hearing impairments may be referred to a Helen Keller program.

BURNS

Destruction of skin tissue that controls temperature, excretes waste, and produces vitamin D via sunlight. Sources of burns may be electrical, thermal, or chemical.

In estimating how much surface is involved in a burn, the Rule of 9s is used. To express the depth of the burn, the terms 1st (superficial), 2nd (partial thickness) and 3rd degree (full thickness) are used. Some burn care centers also use the term "4th degree" when burns extend through the muscle to the bone.

Rule of Nines

(Diagram reprinted from the *Handbook of Severe Disability*, p. 411)

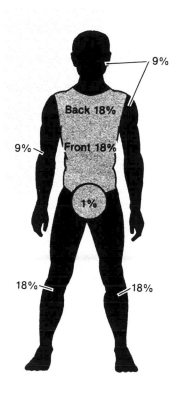

Complications

1.   Contractures - From having joints remain in an abnormal position for extended lengths of time.

2.   Pruritus - Itching

3.   Eye injury - If eyelids or cornea are burned.

4.   Hypertrophic scarring - Cord-like scars that are usually reduced with compression garments such as Jobst garments.

5.   Hair loss - If full-thickness burn of scalp.

6.   Loss of facial member - Due to burns on the face.

Vocational considerations include avoiding occupations which are likely to produce trauma and irritation because burned skin is not as strong as normal skin. This includes avoiding sunlight. Also, if there was smoke inhalation, it is important to avoid dust, smoke, and particles in the air.

Burn patients may have increased sensitivity in the scarred areas and wear pressure garments (Jobst) for up to two years, 23 hours per day. This may cause warmth, so it is important to avoid heat. If person is wearing pressure gloves, dexterity will be limited. If a facial mask is being used, a person may wish to avoid dealing with the public (i.e. receptionist position).

Repeated hospitalization may be necessary for reconstructive surgery. Counseling is recommended, especially if the burned area is exposed when person is dressed. Approximately 85% of burn survivors return to work six months post injury.

CANCER

Cancer cells are cells that multiply beyond normality, overpowering the growth-control mechanism. They result in an uncontrolled cellular mass.

Tumor - A growth of new cells that proliferate without control and serve no useful function. Tumors can be benign or malignant, but are only considered cancerous when they are malignant.

Cancer Terms

> *In-situ* cancer: confined to a duct or lobule

> Sarcomas: Bone, muscle, connective tissue

> Carcinomas: Epithelial cells (skin), lining of lungs and colon, breast

> Leukemias: Blood forming organs

> Lymphomas: Infection fighting organs

Types of Cancer and their Functional Limitations:

Head and Neck Cancer

Surgery may result in some paralysis of muscles important in movement, and postural changes may lead to limitations in reaching and lifting.

Facial disfigurement can occur due to surgery on the face (i.e., removal of eye or ear). This can cause visual field impairments and limit driving. Speech deficits may arise out of surgery in the mouth.

Psychological implications include self-depreciation, depression, and withdrawal from social contact.

Musculoskeletal Cancer

Amputations may be deemed necessary, and chemotherapy and radiation can lead to skin and tissue changes affecting the stump.

Digestive Tract Cancer

Colostomy or ileostomy may be required, and fear of social embarrassment, odors, leakage, and clothing bulges may cause client to withdraw from social and vocational participation.

Leukemia

Characterized by general weakness and limited tolerance for stress and activities requiring energy expenditure. May be vulnerable to bone fractures.

Central Nervous System Cancer

Functional limitations are determined by site of legion (i.e.. spinal cord tumor may cause spinal cord damage/paralysis, and brain tumor may mimic stroke).

Lung Cancer

High morbidity and short life expectancy outweigh most functional limitations. Surgery to remove cancerous tissue can lead to limitations in pulmonary function. Post-operative pain can cause restrictive movement in shoulder and upper arm which in turn leads to postural disturbances and impediments in dressing and bathing.

Genitourinary Cancer

Surgical removal of bladder precludes construction of an ileal conduit and urine is then collected in a bag glued to the skin. Can cause skin irritation, leakage, odors, and cosmetic concerns.

Skin Cancer

If treated prior to local invasion of the cancer, cosmetic problems may be the only functional limitations. If the cancer has spread, other functional deficits may occur depending on the location.

The most important factor to consider in vocational rehabilitation is the site of the cancer, as this determines functional limitations. The counselor should observe physical demands of jobs and match them to the client's physical status and tolerance.

Vocational considerations are most affected by life expectancy. If long-term training is not feasible, it is best to return to former place of employment and modify the job as needed.

CARDIOVASCULAR DISEASES

A.   Coronary Heart Disease

Definition: The building up of fatty material in the coronary artery resulting in a decreased supply of oxygen to the heart.

Causes angina pectoris - heart pain.

If oxygen supply to a portion of the heart is completely interrupted, causes myocardial infarction (M.I.) (heart attack).

Vocational Aspects

The majority of clients who have had an M.I. are able to return to their pre-morbid job, although about one third will require job modifications including less lifting and carrying and avoidance of stressful situations. It is best for these persons to perform sedentary, light, and possibly medium work in environments where extremes of temperature are avoided.

B.   Rheumatic Heart Disease

Definition: Scarring of the heart valves resulting in narrowing of the valve opening and/or incompetent closure of the valve.

Treatment includes antibiotics, and sometimes valve replacement or opening of a stenotic valve. Clients generally take anticoagulants following surgery.

Vocational Aspects

If client is on anticoagulants, must avoid trauma. Physical demands of work are a function of how well the pump functions following surgery. If surgery is successful, should be able to handle medium work.

C.   Hypertension (high blood pressure)

Vocational Aspects

If client has a rapidly accelerating form of hypertension, short-term goals are best. Avoid emotionally stressful situations if they raise blood pressure. Avoid isometric exercise and minimize lifting. For some people, aerobic exercise may also be dangerous. Medications may result in orthostatic symptoms (i.e., dizziness, "blackouts"). If so, avoid jobs requiring balancing and risks of falling. Temperature extremes are not usually a consideration.

D.   IIcart failurc (congcstivc hcart failurc – CIIF)

Definition: May result from any form of heart disease and represents a late stage when the heart's defenses against stress have been overcome.

Vocational Aspects

Medium-range training goals (up to two years) are appropriate. If heart failure is very severe, blood flow to the brain may be decreased, and aptitudes may then be affected. Minimize emotional stress and decrease physical demands (avoid medium, heavy, and very heavy work). Avoid routine climbing. Indoor work is preferred as temperature extremes are not well tolerated. Humidity, noise, and vibrations are okay.

E.   Obliterative Arterial Disease

Definition: Caused by atherosclerosis involving arteries of the abdomen and legs. Slowly progressive.

Claudication: With exertion, client will experience weakness and a tight, cramping due to narrowing of the blood vessels.

Symptoms at rest include numbness, tingling, and continuous pain, especially in toes and feet. If disease is severe, blood supply may be inadequate to maintain extremities and due to ulcers, amputations may then be required.

Buerger's disease: A less common form of obliterative arterial disease seen in men between the ages of 20 and 40 years. It involves small arteries (rather than medium and large), and the feet as well as hands are affected. Fingertip ulcers may appear and necessitate amputations. Visual disturbances also may occur.

Vocational Aspects

Avoid work in cold environments. Minimize walking and climbing. Occupational stress okay. With Buerger's Disease, avoid dexterous hand work, but lifting is okay. Avoid work involving trauma or skin damage as reduced blood supply interferes with wound healing.

F.   Arteriospastic Disorders

1.   Raynaud's Disease - Blueness in hands in response to cold or emotional stimuli. Usually seen in women and begins in the late teens. Tends to involve both hands symmetrically.

2.   Livedo Reticularis - Bluish "fishnet" appearance on skin.

For both of the above, personal care skills may be affected if the client has ulcers on fingertips. In primary forms, plan for long-term goals. In secondary forms, rehabilitation potential is dependent on underlying disease.

G.   Varicose Veins

Definition: Dilated veins in which the valves that keep the blood returning to the heart become incompetent. Causes feelings of heaviness and fatigue in the legs, especially at the end of the day. Edema from the knee down is common.

Vocational Aspects

Minimize time spent standing stationary.

H.   Thrombophlebitis

Definition: Acute disease of the veins characterized by inflammation and clotting, usually in the lower extremities.

Vocational Aspects

Avoid work requiring being on one's feet for long periods of time. May need to be in job where it is possible to elevate feet at times during the day.

Notes regarding exercise:

Aerobic Exercise
Movements which are continuous and rhythmic (walking, jogging, cycling, swimming). Activities are performed with a consumption of increased amounts of oxygen. This is the only form of exertion for which there is any beneficial effect in patients with cardiac disease.

Isometric Exercise
Muscular activity against a fixed, unmoving resistance (carrying a suitcase, lifting weights, working the arms over the head). There is very little increase in heart rate, cardiac output, or oxygen consumed, but there is an increase in blood pressure. Should be avoided by cardiac clients.

Isotonic Exercise
Activities that maintain the same tone in a muscle through a full or partial range of joint motion. Movements are generally rhythmic and continuous (pushing a wheelbarrow). Common in vocational tasks.

CEREBRAL PALSY

Disorders of movement resulting from damage to the brain at some time during its period of growth and development. Manifestations of C.P. depend upon the location and severity of the brain damage.

Causes of CP can be prenatal (e.g. infections, asphyxia, or severe anemia in the mother), natal (e.g. difficulty during delivery resulting in anoxia and subsequent loss of brain tissue), or postnatal (e.g. getting encephalitis during the period immediately following birth). Although some people with CP may experience mental retardation, others may be very bright and each must be assessed individually.

Complications of CP include:

Contractures
Limitations in joint range of motion due to shortening of the muscles or capsules around the joints.

Bowel and Bladder Incontinence
Due to inability to attend or respond to sensory signals indicating the need to void.

Dental Problems
The same factors that caused the brain damage may have also affected developing tooth enamel. Overbites are also common as a result of persistent tongue thrust.

Osteoporosis
Due to deficient muscle activity, insufficiently mineralized bone may result.

Degenerative Joint Disease
Due to abnormal wear and tear on poorly aligned joints.

Scoliosis
An abnormally curved spine may result from poorly supported sitting posture with asymmetrical muscle pull on some portion of the spine.

Malnutrition
Can be due to inability to chew or swallow effectively. Also caused by inability to feed self.

Respiratory Infections
Due to poor coughing ability and inefficient swallowing.

Visual Impairments
Due to specific damage to the occidental cortex.

Auditory Impairments
Results from brain damage blocking the auditory pathways from brain stem to temporal lobe.

Seizures
Have been known to occur in approximately 50% of persons with CP.

Fatigue
Due to motor control and coordination deficits, activities that are relatively automatic require expenditure of an enormous amount of physical and mental energy.

Vocational Considerations
Even though brain damage is present, growth in vocational potential can be expected.

Testing for visual perception, visual-motor performance, verbal performance, and verbal expression is recommended.

Vocational aspects will depend on which complications are present. C.P. is <u>not</u> considered a progressive condition.

CHRONIC PAIN

The individual has little basis for estimating when, or even if, the pain problem and associated disruptions in life will end. Can also include *Chronic Benign Pain Syndrome* which typically refers to pain that is not progressive and/or no cause can be found.

Types of Pain:

Headaches
Headaches can be so severe that they immobilize a person and occur frequently enough to cause major difficulties in routine activities such as employment.

Limb Pain
Often stems from injuries to the upper and lower extremities.

Phantom Pain
Following amputation, painful sensations (sometimes debilitating) of the missing body part are very common. This is not a psychological consequence of amputation.

Pain associated with Spinal Cord Injury – *e.g.,* dysesthesia
May be a sharp, burning pain occurring episodically, or may be a deep, dulling, aching pain tending to persist for days, weeks, or months and can be below the level of injury.

Low Back Pain
Can be soft tissue or nerve injury from "pinched" nerves. Four out of five adults will experience significant low back pain sometime during their life. A common problem from injuries on the job. However, can be a result of aging, arthritis and disease.

To relieve pain if soft tissue (muscles), common treatment is non steroidal anti-inflammatory drugs. If surgery, one option is a laminectomy, which removes a small portion of the bone over the nerve root and/or disc material from under the nerve root to give the nerve root more space. Herniated nucleus pulposis is a condition in which part or all of the soft, gelatinous central portion of an intervertebral disk is forced through a weakened part of the disk, resulting in back pain and nerve root irritation. In most cases, medication and physical therapy will be effective, however some require a diskectomy, or surgical removal.

Complex Regional Pain Syndrome
Complex Regional Pain Syndrome (CRPS), also referred to as Reflex Sympathetic Dystrophy (RSD), is a chronic condition characterized by severe burning pain, pathological

changes in bone and skin, excessive sweating, tissue swelling, and extreme sensitivity to touch. The syndrome is a nerve disorder that occurs at the site of an injury (most often to the arms or legs). It may occur without apparent injury. One visible sign of CRPS near the site of injury is warm, shiny red skin that later becomes cool and bluish. The pain that patients report is out of proportion to the severity of the injury and gets worse, rather than better, over time. Eventually the joints become stiff from disuse, and the skin, muscles, and bone atrophy. The symptoms of CRPS vary in severity and duration. The cause of CRPS is unknown. The disorder is unique in that it simultaneously affects the nerves, skin, muscles, blood vessels, and bones. CRPS is diagnosed primarily through observation of the symptoms. Treatment when delayed may find the disorder spreading to larger portions of the extremity or to another extremity. Many people with this disorder may not be able to work.

Two types

Complex regional pain syndrome Type I:
1. The presence of an initiating noxious event or a cause of immobilization.
2. Continuing pain, allodynia (an exaggerated response to non- harmful stimuli i.e., clothing touching individual) or hyperalgesia (an extreme sensitivity to pain caused by damage to the soft tissue) with which the pain is disproportionate to the inciting event.
3. Evidence at some time of edema, changes in skin blood flow or abnormal sudomotor activity in the painful region.
4. The diagnosis is excluded by the existence of conditions that would otherwise account for the degree of pain and dysfunction.
   NOTE: *Criteria 2, 3 and 4 are necessary for a diagnosis of complex regional pain syndrome.*

Complex regional pain syndrome Type II (causalgia):
1. The presence of continuing pain, allodynia or hyperalgesia after a nerve injury, not necessarily limited to the distribution of the injured nerve.
2. Evidence at some time of edema, changes in skin blood flow or abnormal sudomotor activity in the region of the pain.
3. The diagnosis is excluded by the existence of conditions that would otherwise account for the degree of pain and dysfunction.

Fibromyalgia:
1. An arthritis-related syndrome characterized by widespread or generalized muscular pain, tenderness, and fatigue.

2. Fibromyalgia literally means pain in the muscles, ligaments, and tendons.

Functional Limitations:

Pain may limit extent and duration of body movements such as lifting, bending, twisting, and reaching. Pain medications can interfere with alertness and may cause dizziness, changes in intellectual and cognitive function, or lethargy.

The communication of one's pain to family, co-workers, and others can elicit overly helpful responses. This reaction may reinforce pain behavior.

Clients may be unnecessarily inactive due to fear of incurring additional body damage or pain, and depression is common.

Persons with chronic pain have often been unemployed for many years. Therefore, taking "time out" for further education is risky. Further education is recommended only when acceptable vocational alternatives are not found, and there is compelling evidence that the education will restore and maintain activity level.

Chronic pain is unlikely to influence aptitudes unless some permanent loss of body movement or skill exists due to surgery.

Avoid occupations that are likely to result in recurrence of pain problems. One pain control option is transcutaneous electrical neural stimulation (TENS), which is the application of surface electrodes with the transmission of mild amounts of electricity (controlled by the patient) that theoretically interferes with neurotransmission of pain impulses to the brain.

DIABETES

Definition: A disease of the insulin-producing cells (Islets of Langerhans) of the pancreas causing impaired metabolism of carbohydrates, fats, and proteins. The carbohydrate metabolism deficiency results in a defective ability to utilize glucose, and this results in high blood sugar (hyperglycemia) and glucose in urine (glucosuria).

The Two Types of Diabetes:

Type I (sometimes termed Juvenile Diabetes)
- Usually develops in infancy, adolescence, or young adulthood (but can also occur in adulthood)
- Abrupt onset
- Generally insulin-dependent (aka Insulin Dependent Diabetes Mellitus – IDDM)
- Only 7% of total diabetic population has type I

Type II
- Typically develops in middle or later years
- Typically controlled by diet or oral medication but may progress to insulin injections

Terms associated with Diabetes:

- Polyuria - frequent urination
- Polydipsia - excessive thirst
- Polyphagia - excessive hunger
- Ketoacidosis - The body breaks down fats for fuel because there is no insulin to metabolize glucose. The body is unable to metabolize the breakdown products (ketones). The ketones circulate in the blood and upset the body's acid/base balance.
- Hypoglycemia - Occurs when blood sugar is too low for the amount of insulin taken. It can be caused by decreased carbohydrates and delayed meals.

Complications: (can have effects on the entire body system)

- Visual impairment (can lead to blindness or cataracts)
- Heart problems including high blood pressure
- Vascular difficulty
- Ketoacidosis
- Hypoglycemia
- Stroke
- Gangrene
- Peripheral neuropathy (reduced sensation in extremities).

Vocational Aspects

If free of complications and maintains good control of disease, no diminution of motor and mental skills. If client has peripheral neuropathy, then may have problems sensing texture and handling small objects. If client has stroke, can effect motor and/or mental skills.

Avoid work considered dangerous if blood sugar is not easily controlled, as hypoglycemia may develop. If diabetes is not stable, then avoid work involving heavy machinery, ladders, and construction. Jobs requiring irregular work hours or meal times should be avoided as should working alone (due to possibility of hypoglycemia).

Physical demands are dependent only on client's strength (if client is free of complications), but physical demands should not vary from day to day. If client has severe neuropathy of lower extremities, then avoid excessive standing or walking. If client has neuropathy in hands, then avoid work where thermal or chemical burns may occur. Also, diabetics should avoid occupational hazards because of the difficulty in wound healing associated with the disease.

Due to circulation problems, diabetics with neuropathy, cardiac disease, or vascular disease should not work in environments where dampness, cold temperatures, extreme heat, or abrupt changes in temperature occur. Hands and feet must be protected from burns or frostbite.

DRUG ABUSE

The taking of a substance that modifies one or more of an organism's functions, and leads to physical and/or psychological dependence.

Psychological Dependence
Occurs when a drug produces a feeling of satisfaction that requires continuous administration of the drug to produce pleasure and avoid discomfort.

Physical Dependence
An adaptive state manifested by intense physical disturbances when administration of a drug is suspended. These effects are known as withdrawal.

Tolerance
The drug dependent person requires increased levels of the drug to obtain effects previously experienced with smaller doses. Tolerance may or may not be present during drug abuse.

Drug use can be experimental (use is terminated before dependency occurs), casual (use is discontinuous), or dependent (use is continuous).

Common Types of Drugs

A.   Narcotics

Central nervous system depressants that reduce pain (morphine, heroin, methadone, and codeine).

Psychological aspects include living within an antisocial subculture, and rejection of society. Because narcotics are expensive, users tend to participate in illegal activities (i.e. theft and prostitution) to support their habit. Due to participation in illegal activities, users tend to be unreliable and untruthful. Counselor should identify health problems, family issues, and mental health concerns.

Placement should be viewed as a long-term goal after more realistic intermediate goals of evaluation, work adjustment, and skills training.

B.   Stimulants

Central Nervous System stimulants (cocaine, amphetamines). During use and withdrawal, users may experience paranoid delusions, marked deterioration of personality, or drug-induced psychosis. Persons may be violently antisocial.

Regular urine testing during rehabilitation is strongly recommended, as is termination of user's association with friends in the drug subculture. Also, acceptance of a

113

schedule more appropriate to the working world than to the nightlife of an abuser should be encouraged.

C.   Depressants

Central nervous system depressants that are unlike narcotics because they do not necessarily relieve pain (alcohol, barbiturates, and non-barbiturate sedatives).

If administration of the drug is suddenly discontinued, withdrawal syndrome can be life threatening. It is characterized by delusions, hallucinations, and incoherence.

Rehabilitation potential is based on age, duration of dependence, personal resources (i.e. family, home, and finances), job skills, and concomitant pathology.

Chronic illness is characterized by relapses and remissions; therefore, occasional return to use should be viewed as part of the disease. Confidence of the client in his/her counselor will lead him/her to seek the counselor's help in terminating the episode rather than concealing the transgression.

D.   Hallucinogens

(Psilocybin, mescaline, LSD, PCP)

The lifestyle usually associated with hallucinogen users includes neglect of physical health, poor hygiene, and poor nutrition. Users are unconventional in attitudes and behavior, and they tend to lead unstable lives (regarding school, work, and address). Unemployment tends to be high, and underachievement is common.

The majority of hallucinogen users tend to terminate use within a few years because the "trip" - if repeated many times - loses its appeal.

E.   Cannabis

(Hashish and marijuana) derived from the hemp plant.

Daily use can lead to apathy and indolence, known as the amotivational syndrome. The abuser tends to deal with stress by using cannabis, thus isolating self from painful reality.

F.   Volatile Solvents

(Gasoline, varnish, pain thinner, nitrous oxide)

Users are most often teenage males who, due to this drug use, have upset their psychosexual maturation and education. Extent of the drug use determines rehabilitation potential.

Considerations in vocational counseling include post-employment follow-up as clients attempt to deal with day to day stresses on the job. Clients may have demanding personalities, difficulty with authority figures, and may falsify employment applications. Finally, redirection into a "straight" job can be challenging, because clients probably made more money in illegal activities.

END STAGE RENAL DISEASE (KIDNEY FAILURE)

Uremia
Generalized metabolic abnormality and is the term used to describe the clinical symptoms of end stage renal disease.

These symptoms may include:

- Decreased urine output
- Anemia
- Osteoporosis
- Heart Failure
- Ulcers
- Bleeding from the stomach, mouth, or rectum
- Loss of appetite
- Lethargy
- Nausea
- Vomiting
- Swelling of legs or entire body
- Memory loss
- Difficulty in concentrating
- Peripheral neuropathy with weakness and sensory loss
- Sexual dysfunction
- Occasionally coma and convulsions

The earliest signs of kidney failure are often the inability to concentrate and shortened attention span. As a result, persons with mentally demanding jobs often change occupations to jobs less exacting.

As kidney failure becomes more severe, physical impairment becomes evident. It is then that persons involved with physically demanding work may have difficulty on the job.

If peripheral neuropathy develops, client may have difficulty with walking, climbing stairs, and balance. Grip strength and writing ability may also be impaired. If anemia is present, client will have a decreased ability to participate in physical activities.

Uremia may interfere with brain function and result in decreased ability to concentrate. This can usually be corrected with dialysis.

Clients on hemodialysis (a painful and several times per week experience) will need retraining if former job involved heavy manual labor. Training lasting from three months to one year is appropriate. Retraining into a highly complicated field should be discouraged due to decreased concentration and attention. There are other forms of dialysis which are less functionally impairing, but are expensive. Traditional hemodialysis is free.

Clients with a kidney transplant will have fewer problems that interfere with work, but due to the danger of infection, they must avoid jobs where infection may occur. Excessive bending must also be avoided in order to keep from damaging the kidney. Depression is common because clients are unable to return to their "normal" life.

EPILEPSY/SEIZURE DISORDERS

Characterized by unexplained, recurring seizures (occasional, excessive disorderly discharge of electricity in neuronal tissues of the brain).

Focus - The location of the brain where the seizure starts.

Aura - Premonitory symptoms that occur just before a seizure and may "give warning" that a seizure is coming.

Types of Seizures:

A.   Focal Seizure
      The electrical discharge remains localized, and its effects are thus limited to the areas of the body controlled by the focus.

B.   Jacksonian Seizure
      A focal seizure that originates in the motor cortex.

C.   Grand Mal Seizure (also called Tonic Clonic)
      A seizure that spreads widely through the brain circuits and has few localizing features.

D. Petit Mal Seizures
Arises from deep within the brain core rather than from a focal point on the surface of the brain. Characterized by brief lapses of consciousness or "staring spells."

E. Psychomotor Seizures
The electrical discharge starts in one temporal lobe and is manifested by autonomic motor activity and alterations in behavior which may be bizarre.

Vocational considerations include understanding how the seizure disorder may specifically affect functioning on a job. Information regarding possible precipitators of a seizure (i.e. fatigue, flickering/fluorescent lights, stress) should be carefully noted when evaluating a potential occupation or worksite.

Clients should avoid working around heights and potentially dangerous machinery, as people often fall when a seizure occurs.

Co-worker education is important because the client may have a seizure while on the job, and long-term planning is appropriate. State laws vary regarding the length of time a person must be seizure free for drivers license eligibility, but one year is common. There are generally no physical limitations unless caused by seizure medications.

HARD OF HEARING, LOSS OF HEARING AND DEAFNESS

A reduction in sensitivity to sounds which may be accompanied by some loss in the ability to correctly interpret auditory stimuli, even when amplified.

A. Conductive Hearing Loss
Arises from defects in the auditory system which interferes with sound waves reaching the cochlea. May be corrected with a cochlear implant or improved with a hearing aid.

B. Sensorineural Hearing Loss
Caused by defects to the auditory pathways within the central nervous system. Associated with aging.

C. Mixed Hearing Loss
Involves both conductive and sensorineural hearing deficits.

D. Prevocational Deafness
Hearing loss that takes place before the age of 19.

117

E.   Prelingual Deafness
Hearing loss that takes place before learning language (infant or toddler).

F.   Telecommunications Device for the Deaf (TDD also referred to as TTY)
Whatever is typed on he originating machine is transmitted via telephone to the receiving machine, which types the message. This has contributed significantly to the vocational potential of deaf clients.

Functional limitations are dependent upon degree of impairment and age of onset. In general, the greater the loss of ability to distinguish single words and the earlier the age of onset, the greater the rehabilitation challenge.

Clients still in school will require instructional materials in which the content is visual. Speech instruction is an especially important aspect of education. Prelingually deaf or hearing impaired children can learn to speak with the use of technology.

American Sign Language, which uses symbols (ASL) and Manual English or Signing Exact English in which exact English is signed, are the two forms of sign language most often utilized by persons who are deaf.

Along with TDDs, other useful devices that broaden vocational options include flashing lights to replace audio signals. If loudspeakers, buzzers, or other auditory devices are used in the workplace, counselor should ensure that client can receive the information in a non-auditory manner.

Good lighting in the workplace is important for lip-reading. Avoid working in a noisy environment because the noise source can create vibrations that are uncomfortable and distracting to persons who are deaf. It is also important to avoid noisy environments because prolonged exposure to loud sounds can add to a hearing loss and interferes with a person's ability to use "feeling" as an alternative sense.

An interpreter may be needed from intake to job placement if counselor is unable to sign.

HEMOPHILIA

A group of congenital, inherited disorders in which the blood coagulation factor does not function. The blood does not clot, so bleeding continues.

1.   Type A - Factor VIII deficiency (most common type)

2.   Type B - Factor IX deficiency (also known as Christmas Disease and is less common)

3.   Other rare coagulation diseases including Von Willebrand's Disease

Physical limitations include limited range of motion, chronic pain, limited mobility, and hemoarthritis (bleeding into the joints).

There may be a restricted ability to climb steps or perform heavy manual tasks. Prolonged sitting and standing can also be difficult. Individuals can drive, but if physical limitations are severe, hand controls may be needed.

May also require assistive devices including splints, canes, and ankle supports.

Psychosexual aspects include dependence on (often overprotective) parents. Individuals may also go through a period of denial as teenagers, and engage in risk-taking behavior.

Previously, absenteeism has been a problem for hemophiliacs involved in work training programs or school, but improved medical technology is decreasing medical complications and time out of work and school for these patients. In evaluating any job for a hemophiliac, major joint involvement must be evaluated.

Special note:

It is estimated that more than 85% of those who were hemophiliacs in 1985 are HIV positive due to contaminated blood supplies in past years.

MENTAL DISABILITIES or DISORDERS

The grouping of psychoses, neuroses, organic brain syndromes and personality disorders that present as difficulties in intellect and behavior. (Note: reportedly it is helpful if you know what medications are used with various disorders)

A.   Schizophrenia/Psychotic Disorders (thought disorders)
        1. Schizophrenia
        An upheaval from within the personality, a fragmenting of the mental functions, an overwhelming experience that separates thought, mood, and behavior from reality. Characteristic symptoms include:

* Positive Symptoms: "Added experiences", Events and experiences others do not have. (E.g., Delusions e.g., false beliefs, hallucinations e.g., seeing, hearing, smelling or feeling things that are not there).

- Negative Symptoms: "Removed experiences", Experiences, events, feelings removed from normal experience. (E.g., lack of motivation or life pleasure, flat affect, apathy)

- Cognitive Symptoms: range of deficits affecting various cognitive functions.

- Psychosis: break with reality

    1.1   Paranoid Type - Delusions of persecution or grandeur.

    1.2   Disorganized Type – Disorganized speech and/or behavior.

    1.3   Catatonic - Excessive, sometimes violent motor activity, total inhibition of movement, or extreme negativism.

    1.4   Undifferentiated - Symptoms of one or more of the above.

    1.5   Residual Type – Absence of prominent delusions, hallucinations, disorganized speech, and grossly disorganized or catatonic behavior but there is continuing evidence of disturbance (e.g., odd beliefs or unusual perceptual experiences).

    2. Schizophreniform – Symptoms similar to schizophrenia above. Episodes last at least 1 month but less than 6 months.

    3. Schizoaffective – Includes major depression or manic or mixed episodes with symptoms similar to schizophrenia. Can be classified as bipolar type or depressive type.

    4. Delusional – Includes non-bizarre delusions but clients have symptoms similar to schizophrenia although functioning is not markedly impaired. Types include Erotomanic, grandiose, jealous, persecutory, somatic, mixed and unspecified.

    5. Brief psychotic disorder - Symptoms similar to schizophrenia lasting at least 1 day but not more than 1 month.

    6. Shared Psychotic disorder (Folie a Deux) – Two people have similar delusions.

    7. Psychotic disorder due to…. (indicate the general medical condition).

    8. Substance-induced psychotic disorder.

    9. Psychotic disorder not otherwise specified.

B.   Mood Disorders

1. Major depressive - Only depressive episodes occur.

2. Manic episode - Only manic episodes occur.

3. Mixed episode - Occurrence of alternating manic and depressive episodes.

4. Hypomanic disorder– Inflated self esteem or grandiosity and deceased need for sleep.

5. Dysthymic disorder– depressed mood for most of the day, for more days than not.

6. Bi-polar disorder – dramatic mood swings—from overly "high" and/or irritable to sad and hopeless, and then back again, often with periods of normal mood in between.

7. Cyclothymic disorder – Numerous periods with hypomanic symptoms, but not as severe as bi-polar.

8. Mood disorder due to … - (indicate the general medical condition).

9. Substance-induced mood disorder.

10. Mood disorder not otherwise specified.

C.   Anxiety Disorders

Preoccupation with anxiety.

1. Panic Attack – Sudden onset of intense apprehension, fearfulness, or terror, often associated with feelings of impending doom.

2. Phobic - Irrational fear of object or situation leading to an avoidance behavior.

3. Obsessive-Compulsive - Intrusion of unwanted thoughts or actions unable to stop. Obsessions = thoughts, compulsions = actions.

4. Post Traumatic Stress Disorder (PTSD). Re-experiencing of an extremely traumatic event accompanied by symptoms of increase arousal and by avoidance of stimuli associated with trauma. May have dreams and sleep disturbance.

5. Generalized Anxiety Disorder – At least 6 months of persistent and excessive anxiety and worry.

D.   Personality Disorders

1. Paranoid Personality Disorder – Pattern of distrust and suspiciousness.

2. Antisocial Personality – Sociopath. Pattern of disregard for, and violation of, the rights of others.

3. Dependent Personality – Submissive and clinging behavior related to an excessive need to be taken care of.

4. Schizoid Personality – Pattern of detachment from social relations and a restricted range of emotional expressions.

5. Histrionic Personality – Pattern of excessive emotionality and attention seeking.

6. Narcissistic Personality – Pattern of grandiosity, need for admiration and lack of empathy.

7. Borderline Personality - Pattern of volatility or instability in interpersonal relationships, self-image, affect, and marked impulsively. Sometimes referred to as bordering on psychosis.

8. Avoidant personality disorder – Pervasive pattern of social inhibition, feelings of inadequacy, hypersensitivity to negative evaluation.

Drug therapy is the most common and effective treatment of mental illness.

Vocational considerations include adjusting work goals (i.e., an MBA with two psychotic episodes would be advised to lower her work goals to achievable levels). Individuals will have few physical limitations but will have difficulty dealing with stress. Repeated hospitalizations may alternate with acceptable mental functioning, so encourage persons with mental illness to continue psychiatric treatment even after returning to work. Post-employment follow-up is very important, especially during the first few months. Borderline personalities may be difficult to trust and typically have stormy relationships.

DSM-IV

Multiaxial Assessment

Axis I - Clinical Disorders

- Usually diagnosed as child or adolescent

- Does not include mental retardation

- Due to general medical condition.

- Includes medication induced movement disorders

- Mental disorder such as mood, anxiety, sleep, adjustment, schizophrenia., etc.

Axis II -Personality & Mental Retardation

- More "stable"

- Examples: Paranoid, Obsessive Compulsive, Schizoid, Narcissistic, Dependent

Axis III -General Medical Conditions

- Medical diagnosis, if any.

Axis IV - Psychosocial & Environmental

- Death of significant person

- Academic, school discord

- Unemployment, stressful work

- Homelessness, poverty

- Arrest, crime victim, litigation

Axis V – GAF (Global Assessment of Functioning)

- Psychological, social and vocational functioning

- Scale of 1 to 100 (1=lowest)

- "0" means inadequate information

- Does NOT include physical or environmental limitations

MENTAL RETARDATION

A significantly subaverage general intellectual functioning existing concurrently with deficits in adaptive behavior manifested during the developmental period. Onset before 21, etiology unknown (in 75% of cases).

Instruments generally used to determine Mental Retardation:

1. Stanford Binet
2. Wechsler

Relationship between IQ and level of impairment:

Level	Stanford-Binet	Wechsler
Mild	52-68	55-69
Moderate	36-51	40-54
Severe	20-35	25-39
Profound	19 and lower	24 and lower

Vocational considerations include utilizing work samples, and training programs that focus on social skills. Persons with MR learn best when the education is highly structured and direct. Poor social skills- rather than problems related to job tasks - are often the main reasons a client may lose a job. Standard vocational testing is less accurate than on-the-job evaluation or work samples. Job coaching in competitive employment settings and use of "natural supports" has been shown to be successful. Although on their way out, sheltered workshops are still used in some places especially for work adjustment (training personal work habits such as arriving on time, proper hygiene, cooperating with others, learning to accept supervision, etc.).

MULTIPLE SCLEROSIS

Breakdown of the myelin sheath in the brain and spinal cord which causes loss of muscle control, spasms, ataxia, loss of coordination of muscles especially extremities, and often cognitive deficits. Has unknown origin, and is characterized by a series of exacerbations and remissions for some, and down hill progression for others. However, many people with MS are never seriously incapacitated. There is no cure. Medication may reduce symptoms.

The life expectancy is essentially the same but due to the fatigue factor, individuals should avoid heavy physical work. Sedentary work should not include fine hand movements (i.e., writing) because tremor/ataxia may develop. It is also wise to avoid work where a lot of moving around from point A to point B is required. Sedentary work indoors, where it is not too hot, is optimal. (Most people with significant MS function poorly in warm environments.) In late stages of MS, disturbances in mental abilities (the learning of new material) may develop.

NEUROMUSCULAR DISEASES

These diseases affect the motor system, and they cause weakness or clumsiness (with the exception of Guillain-Barré). Cause is unknown, sensation is unaffected, and communication is not affected until the late stages, if at all. These diseases are progressive unless otherwise noted.

A.   Huntington's Disease

Adult onset (between age 30 -50). Characterized by a loss of fine motor dexterity, involuntary movement, and mental deterioration. Duration of onset to death is approximately 15 years.

Symptoms are increased in intensity by emotional stress or concentration on performance of physical tasks.

B.   Parkinson's Disease

Occurs in older adults. Characterized by muscle rigidity and slowness of movement. Generally 10-20 years from onset to severe disability.

Driving is impaired, so transportation to and from work may be one of the biggest problems. Need to avoid cold (because it increases stiffness), automobile high traffic areas (because carbon monoxide has been linked to this disease), and stressful occupations (because this increases the tremors). Persons in white collar work can continue for a long time, unlike persons involved with physical labor.

C.   Friedreich's Ataxia

Spinal cord and cerebellar degeneration. Onset usually takes place at the age of 13, and many are severely incapacitated by their mid-20's. Ataxia (clumsiness) may be the earliest sign. The heart and respiratory complications that follow will lead to death.

Fine motor skills, speech, and balance is affected. Mobility limitations result in need for wheelchair, and individuals should avoid dangerous surroundings. Work can consist of light physical demands only.

D.   Amyotrophic Lateral Sclerosis (ALS)

"Freezing up" of muscles. Survival after onset is from 6 to 8 years.

Communication skills are unaffected, and light/sedentary demands are appropriate. Fine motor skills may be unaffected, but grip strength and lifting ability will be diminished. Adaptation of current job or short-term goals (6 - 12 months) are appropriate.

E.   Spinal Muscular Atrophy

Hereditary childhood disease characterized by degeneration of the anterior horns. May be detected in infancy when "floppy infant" occurs, and survival into teens is unlikely.

If individual does survive into teens, social retardation and extreme physical dependency may limit potential for gainful employment.

F.   Polio/Late Effects of Polio

Acute virus of the spinal cord causing muscle paralysis. The disease is not progressive, but polio survivors can experience new muscle involvement 40 years later leading to reduce ability to physically function.

Many polio survivors have grown to be "over-achieving" adults in professional and high-ranking positions. The new muscle involvement can present unusually great psychological as well as physical challenges. Alteration in work schedule is often required to accommodate fatigue/muscle weakness.

G.   Guillain-Barré

Damaged myelinated sheath. Damage is limited to motor impairment, is not necessarily progressive, and may actually improve. Often precipitated by an infection, and maximum paralysis occurs within one to three weeks. Respiratory arrest may take place, and if acute degeneration has occurred, improvement will take place only very slowly (years).

Intelligence and communication are unimpaired, but there will be a loss of fine motor dexterity. If paralysis is severe, functional limitations are similar to spinal cord injury.

H.   Myasthenia Gravis

Affects the thymus gland. Characterized by drooping eyelids and muscle fatigue, with exacerbations/remissions. If treated, individuals can live productively for 5 to 20 years.

Re-education to less physically demanding jobs may be necessary. It is also recommended to avoid cold environments.

I.   Muscular Dystrophy

A family of hereditary diseases that cause degenerative changes in the muscles. The most common MDs are Duchenne and childhood muscular dystrophy. All are chronic and progressive. Typically people die from the complications associated with these diseases, not the disease itself. The past rate of deterioration is a good predictor for future deterioration. Clients with these diseases will typically have difficulty protecting themselves from extreme weather.

Educational planning must take into account life expectancy. Work requiring sedentary or light demands is recommended.

PERIPHERAL NEUROPATHIES

Diseases of the peripheral nervous system (i.e., the nerves) located outside of the brain and spinal cord. They are caused by toxins (i.e., lead, carbon monoxide, heroin), cancer (due to a tumor near a nerve), internal mechanical trauma (constriction caused by a ruptured disc), excessive use of alcohol (disrupts nerve messages), or an external trauma (stabbing).

Peripheral neuropathies can be mostly sensory, mostly motor, or a combination of both. They can involve one nerve, several nerves, or all of the peripheral nerves.

Vocational considerations take into account the location of disease. If lower extremity nerves are involved, the individual will most likely have weakness and sensory loss in the lower extremities, which results in decreased ambulation and balance skills.

If there is upper extremity involvement, weakness and sensory loss in the hands is common and this will cause limitations in eating and dressing.

Finger/hand dexterity, eye/hand coordination, and eye/hand/foot coordination may be limited due to sensory impairment, therefore avoid jobs where person cannot see his or her hands (i.e., repairing objects where it is necessary to reach into an unseen place).

Persons with reduced sensation should avoid working around flames or hot objects as they may unknowingly incur accidental burns.

Peripheral neuropathies usually stabilize or improve*; therefore, long-term planning is appropriate (2 or more years training). The pain, sensory loss, ambulation problems, and weakness in the extremities can often be compensated for with training or adaptive equipment.

*Peripheral neuropathies caused by heredity may progress, but progression is slow enough to still allow for at least two years of educational planning.

127

PULMONARY DYSFUNCTION

A.   Chronic Obstructive Pulmonary Disease (COPD)

1.   Chronic Bronchitis
Chronic inflammation of the bronchial tubes, with increased quantities of mucus and mucus-secreting cells.

2.   Emphysema
Breakdown of the alveolar walls, with enlargement of the alveoli. Usually caused by chronic bronchitis.

Persons with COPD may be either:

1.   Blue Bloaters
Characterized by production of mucus, a conspicuous cough, expectoration (to cough up and spit out), and wheezing.

2.   Pink Puffers
"Dry," with little or no mucus. Emphysema is dominant.

Functional limitations of COPD may include impairments in walking, dressing, bathing, and speech due to dyspnea (difficulty breathing). Driving is possible, but walking to and from the car may be difficult. Stair climbing is restricted when disease is moderate. Dyspnea can result in fear.

Vocational implications include the need to receive ongoing medical treatment if employment is to be maintained. Cough and expectoration may be considered a cosmetic impairment to working with close interpersonal interaction.

Blue bloaters are prone to periodic exacerbations; therefore, absenteeism may be expected. Also, any client with severe COPD will probably require some accommodation for absenteeism.

Sedentary occupations are recommended, and if occasional greater levels of energy are required (e.g. walking to the mailroom one time per day with a bundle of outgoing mail) then a rest period to follow is recommended (or job modification). It is crucial to analyze all physical demands of a potential job, no matter how intermittent they may be.

Extremes or sudden changes in temperature, exposure to adverse weather conditions, extremes of dryness or humidity, and dust or irritating gasses should be avoided.

B.   Asthma

Characterized by bronchospasm, edema of the bronchial walls, infiltration of the bronchial wall with eosinophil cells, and production of excessive mucus.

No activity is possible during an attack (which can lead to death), as breathing in itself takes up all the client's energy. Between attacks, however, the client usually has no functional limitations (given the absence of other disabilities).

Jobs with irritant-free environments and few physical demands are desirable. Long-term goals can be considered if attacks are well controlled. Absenteeism due to attacks needs to be accommodated, and employer/co-worker education is important in order to point out that an attack is rarely (if ever) life threatening.

Industrial Asthma
A particular occupation seems to induce an asthma attack in a worker (e.g. meat packing, baking, and exposure to certain fibers or agricultural products). A job change is usually necessary.

C.   Occupational Lung Disease

Occurs when occupational fumes and dusts (e.g. chemicals used in rubber or plastic industries) chronically irritate the nasal and respiratory membranes.

Vocational considerations are similar to those in COPD, but the long duration of client exposure required before disability occurs brings most persons into vocational rehabilitation late in their careers (ages 50-60).

D.   Cystic Fibrosis

A hereditary disorder in which many mucus-secreting organs are damaged by thick mucus which blocks ducts and leads to degeneration and scarring of the organs, particularly the pancreas and lungs. Life expectancy has improved substantially due to improvement in symptom and complication management. There is no cure. Median survival in 2006 was 37 years with many patients having families and productive careers. Functional capabilities are highly variable and each person should be individually assessed. Performance limitations are most noticeable with the pulmonary and digestion tract complications.

Airway clearance therapies to dislodge mucus are required daily. Daily care requirements are essential and usually increase with more severe disease. One person from the article below needed 6 hours/day of therapy. Coughing can interfere with talking as a condition of employment (e.g., telemarketing). Pulmonary dysfunction may limit physical work capacity.

Vocational considerations include support services to patients and their families to assure good care, vocational achievement and quality of life. Individuals with CF may need to have food at their work site because of typical need for nutrition supplements. Environments with smokers, auto exhaust, many fumes or odors, and volatile chemicals should be avoided. Environments with frequent exposure to viruses and other infections, such as day care centers, teaching school, or some healthcare centers may not be suitable for someone with CF.

Major complications for individuals with CF include hypoxia, pneumothorax and hemoptysis. Supplemental oxygen may be needed and can increase length and quality of life, and extend work life potential. In the article below, patients with skilled jobs were more likely to have maintained their positions than those with unskilled jobs. When possible, assisting individuals with CF in pursuing education is recommended.

For more detailed overview see Mungle, J., Burker, E. & Yankaskas, J. (2002). Vocational rehabilitation for adolescents and adults with cystic fibrosis. *Journal of Applied Rehabilitation Counseling, 33*(4), 15-21. or www.cff.org

RHEUMATIC DISEASES

This group includes all diseases and syndromes that involve joints (primarily synovial). Some of these conditions occur irregularly and constitute a minor problem. These diseases are systemic and thought to be a viral reaction.

A.   Rheumatoid Arthritis

This systemic inflammation of the synovial joints is seen most often in children under the age of four, and adults over 40. Synovial joints allow motion and bear weight; therefore, motion is restricted, and weight bearing can be a problem. Symptoms typically progress and persist.

Associated complications include:

1.   Carpal Tunnel Syndrome - Numbness, tingling, and loss of feeling in thumb, index finger, and middle finger.

2.   Sjogren's Syndrome - Invasion of the lymphocytes often resulting in dry eyes and mouth.

3.   Peripheral Neuropathy - Numbness, tingling, and loss of function in fingers and toes.

4.   Pleural Effusion - Mild accumulations of scars in the lungs.

5.   Baker's Cyst - Inflamed synovial fluid escapes from the knee and collects in the space behind the knee.

6.   Anemia - Results in weakness. It has two causes: 1) Chronic inflammation can affect the production of red cells in bone marrow, and 2) Medication can lead to low-grade blood leakage from stomach walls.

Vocational implications include avoiding manual labor as it may cause exacerbations. Motor coordination, finger and hand dexterity, and eye/hand/foot coordination may be adversely affected. Vocational training of two to four years should be considered. Activities of an abstract, creative nature (rather than routine, organized activity) should be encouraged if such aptitudes are present, as repetitive mechanized motions may induce overuse of inflamed joint.

B.   Ankylosing Spondylitis

A form of inflammatory joint disease which affects the joints and ligaments of the spine. This freezing/fusing of the spine typically starts at the bottom of the spine and moves up.

The bony bridges reduce motor functioning and may limit the ability to breath, but intellect is not affected. The stiff back limits twisting, and reaching and bending should be avoided. Motor coordination and eye/hand/foot coordination are not generally affected. Jobs allowing for frequent position change are optimal, and stressful situations should be avoided as these may lead to back pain. It is important not to attempt to lift over 15 pounds. Jobs with noise, vibration, and dust should not pose a problem.

C.   Degenerative Joint Disease (Osteoarthritis)

This is confined to particular joints as opposed to being systemic, and it causes pain associated with bone spurs and bone-on-bone contact.

The individual can usually continue the present job or related job unless it requires dexterity or heavy use of the involved joint. Use of the involved joint should be limited. In many persons with DJD, climbing, balancing, stooping, and kneeling may be impaired.

SICKLE CELL DISEASE

A deformity of the red blood cells genetically caused and characterized by the presence of gene mutations which produce abnormal hemoglobins. It occurs most often in African Americans (but not always), and each case is very different.

Complications:

A. Pain - Pain crisis from poor blood flow is a common reason for hospitalizations.

B. Eye Problems - Due to infarction of retina.

C. Kidney Disease - Renal failure is one of the most common causes of death in adults with Sickle Cell Disease.

D. Bone Disease - Due to involvement of the bones and joints in the vasocclusive process.

E. Leg Ulcers - Due to infarcts in the skin.

F. Liver Disease - Due to accumulation of iron resulting from transfusions or long-term iron therapy.

G. Priapism - A painful, persistent erection in the penis from sickle cell build up.

H. Lung Disease - Includes pneumonia.

In the presence of renal disease, the potential for rehabilitation should be evaluated in view of the complete unpredictability of chronic organ damage that may occur at a later date.

To define the individual's work capacity, evaluation by an O.T., P.T., or in a sheltered work environment is recommended. There is usually a high fatigue factor due to the anemia with accompanying pain and reduced exertional capacity. Fine motor dexterity is often lessened by joint disease and neurological dysfunction. Also, if neurological deficits exist, person should be directed to sedentary work only. If neurological deficits are not present, person may also perform light work.

Indoor work is preferable as it is important to avoid excessive humidity, cold, moisture, and excessive heat. It is also recommended to avoid stressful occupations, as stress can lead to a sickle cell crisis. Working at lower altitudes is recommended due to poor oxygenation of the blood supply. May have frequent short hospitalizations due to "sickle cell crisis" event.

SPINA BIFIDA

Spina bifida is a neural tube defect (NTD). There are 3 types of NTDs: anencephaly, encephalocele, and spina bifida.

Spina bifida results from the failure of the spine to close properly during the first month of pregnancy, probably from a lack of folic acid. In severe cases, the spinal cord protrudes through the back and may be covered by skin or a thin membrane. Surgery to close a newborn's back is generally performed within 24 hours after birth to minimize the risk of infection and to preserve existing function in the spinal cord.

Because of the paralysis resulting from the damage to the spinal cord, people born with spina bifida may need surgeries and other extensive medical care. The condition can also cause bowel and bladder complications. A large percentage of children born with spina bifida also have hydrocephalus, the accumulation of fluid in the brain. Hydrocephalus is controlled by a surgical procedure called "shunting," which relieves the fluid build up in the brain by redirecting it into the abdominal area. Most children born with spina bifida live well into adulthood as a result of today's sophisticated medical techniques.

Clients with spina bifida need to learn mobility skills, and often use crutches, braces, or wheelchairs. Spina bifida can have a profound effect on the child's emotional and social development. The functional abilities vary widely, so clients need to be individually assessed.

Source: http://www.sbaa.org/html/sbaa_facts.html

SPINAL CORD INJURY

An injury to the spinal cord producing either tetraplegia (aka quadriplegia) (involvement of upper and lower extremities) or paraplegia (involving only the lower extremities). The involvement of extremities can include paralysis and/or loss of sensation. The level of injury and whether it is complete or incomplete will determine residual functioning.
- C1 – C8 results in tetraplegia (quadriplegia)
- T1 and below results in paraplegia.
- C5 and above causes reduced respiratory function.

It is important to know the levels of injury and the effects on functioning (see below). For example, a person with ASIA level C, C-4 will need a power chair and a person with T-8, will need a manual chair. There are products to help people with reduced functioning such as a universal cuff for a C-6 injury to help with loss of hand functioning.

133

Complications
- Paralysis
- Loss of sensation
- Loss of bladder control
- Increased risk of urinary tract infections
- Increased risk of chronic bilateral obstructive nephropathy
- Loss of bowel control
- Loss of sexual functioning
- Paralysis of breathing muscles
- Increased risk of injury to numb areas of the body
- Pain
- Skin breakdown (decubitus)
- Pulmonary infections
- Deep vein thrombosis
- Blood pressure fluctuations

ASIA Scale (American Spinal Cord Injury Association – aka Modified Frankel Scale)

Class A: Complete spinal cord injury: No motor or sensory function is preserved in the sacral segments S4-S5.

Class B: Incomplete spinal cord injury: Sensation but not motor function preserved below the level of injury, and include the sacral segments S4-S5.

Class C: Incomplete spinal cord injury: Motor function is preserved below the neurological level, and more than half of key muscles below the neurological level have a muscle grade less than 3 (Grades 0-2). No functional motor strength.

Class D: Incomplete spinal cord injury. Motor function is preserved below the neurological level, and at least half of the key muscles below the neurological level are graded at 3 or more. The person may be able to use the motor function, for example, for a brief transfer, or ambulate short distances.

Class E: Complete return of all motor and sensory function below the level of the lesion, but may have abnormal reflexes.

Incomplete Syndromes:
1. Central cord syndrome. Paralysis greater in the upper extremity than the lower extremities.
2. Brown-Sequard syndrome. Loss of sensation on one side of the body and loss of motor function on the other side
3. Cauda equina syndrome. Loss of bowel and bladder control and weakness of the lower extremities or paralysis.
4. Conus medullaris syndrome. Areflexic bladder and bowels, and lower limb paralysis.

5. Anterior cord syndrome. Produces variable loss of motor function and of sensitivity to pinprick and temperature while preserving ability to know where the body is in space (proprioception).

The vertebrae are as follows:

1. Cervical   C1-C8
2. Thoracic   T1-T12
3. Lumbar   L1-L5
4. Sacral   S1-S5
5. Coccyx

(Figure reprinted from *Handbook of Severe Disability*, p. 65)

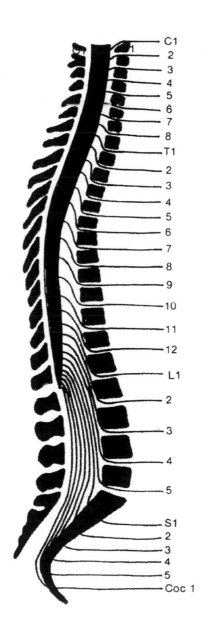

Spinal Cord Nerve Distribution

(Figure reprinted from *Handbook of Severe Disability*, p. 68.)

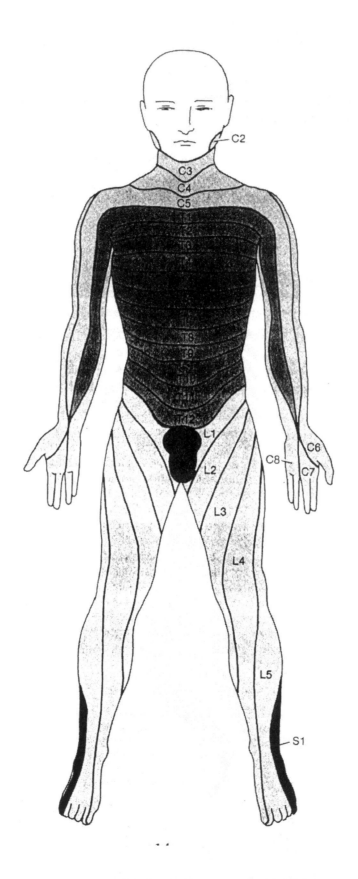

Complications:

1. Decubitus Ulcers - Pressure sores due to the inability of client to shift his or her weight due to paralysis, and due to the absence of pain when lying too long in one position without moving. These sores can require surgery accompanied by weeks or months of bed rest. This will typically disrupt school, work, and/or leisure activities.

2. Infection in lungs, often pneumonia. Respiratory complications are the #1 cause of death in SCI.

3. Spasticity - Involuntary motor activity that interferes with dressing, transfers, bladder function, and skin care.

4. Autonomic Dysreflexia – (T6 and above) Sudden increase in blood pressure with profuse sweating and flushing, usually caused by over distention of bowel or bladder.

5. Genitourinary infections - Due to kidney infections or bladder distention. Also caused by improper positioning or urethral catheter.

Vocational considerations include evaluating the pre-injury worksite for accessibility, and utilizing job modification techniques, adaptive equipment, and computerized work stations.

Tetraplegics and high paraplegics will have reduced capacity to cough, so it is important to avoid occupations that involve dust or foreign particles in the air.

Typically, SCI clients are men between the ages of 18 and 35 who were involved in physical occupations. Training and transition to a sedentary/light occupation can be challenging. In general, the more educated the person with SCI is, the more employable he/she is.

STROKE/BRAIN INJURY

A normally functioning brain, consistent with age, is acutely damaged either by a disruption in blood flow (stroke or cerebral vascular accident) or by tissue damage caused by a blow or lesion of any sort. Strokes (cerebral vascular accidents or brain attacks) can be caused by two basic reasons:
1. Blockage (obstruction or ischemic)
    Cerebral embolus (could be post surgery complication)
    Thrombus (blood clot)

2. Hemorrhage (bleed)
     Aneurysm
     Hypertension
     Vascular malformation

Brain damage can result in behavioral deficits which may include a decrease in physical abilities, intellectual performance, social functioning, emotional control, or any combination of the four.

Prognosis is dependent on:

A.   Severity and Magnitude of the Lesion
The more tissue lost, the higher the probability of significant deficits. The longer the coma, the greater the probability of permanent deficits and severity of impairment.

B.   Premorbid Functioning
Personality characteristics are not so much changed by cerebral damage as they are exaggerated.

C.   Family support

Left cerebral damage results in motor and sensory involvement on the right side of the body (paralysis on the right side of the body is known as right hemiplegia). Language function may also be impaired, therefore, when teaching such a client, spoken instructions may need to be supplemented by pantomime.

Aphasia - Disorders of the language processing centers in the brain.

Right cerebral damage results in motor and sensory involvement on the left side of the body. Intellectual functions including depth perception, intuition, and non-verbal perception may also be impaired (visuospatial deficits or perceptual deficits).

Vocational Implications
Some clients have severe memory loss and cognitive impairments. The ability to learn new information is a common pervasive problem. Cognitive impairments include physiologically based personality disorders. With strokes, language impairments can be a severe problem.

Clients may have use of only one hand and are therefore limited in lifting, carrying, pushing, and pulling. Climbing, balancing, and stooping may also be difficult. With these limitations present, sedentary or light work is best.

Lack of speed may be evident, and the pressure of having to hurry may further decrease speed.

Clients with right cerebral damage perform best in an uncluttered environment with good lighting and minimal distractions.

Waiting until maximum recovery has been reached (with stroke this is at least six months and with brain injury, up to two years) prior to job placement is strongly recommended in order to decrease chances of failure.

A client with a brain injury (and mental illness) is usually more difficult to place in long term employment than clients with other disabilities.

Clients may initially have aphasia, which is the inability to comprehend or produce communication. He or she may also demonstrate perseveration, which is repeating the same behavior or story over and over without the awareness that they have already made the statement.

Scales used during brain injury rehabilitation:

1. Rancho Los Amigos Levels of Cognitive Functioning – Revised
    These levels apply specifically to people with brain injuries and are used in rehabilitation facilities to describe the level of functioning. Ranges from Level I (No response) to Level X (Purposeful, Appropriate). (Note: The old scale was I to VIII)

2. Glasgow Coma Scale
    This scale is typically assessed by ambulance crew, emergency room staff, and during an injured patient's initial hospital stay. The score may also be noted on an ambulance report or emergency room initial assessment. The scale ranges from 3 (Does not open eyes; has no motor response to pinch; makes no noise) to 15 (Opens own eyes; follows simple commands; carries on conversation and is oriented to time and place). The Glasgow Coma Scale level is thought to be a good predictor of severity of brain injury.

TOURETTE'S SYNDROME

A disorder that is diagnosed prior to age 18 where there are either motor and/or vocal tics. Can cause significant impairment in social and occupational functioning. The disorder is not due to the effects of substances or general medical condition.

FUNCTIONAL LIMITATIONS: GENERAL

1. Mobility Limitation
    The function of getting from one location to another is limited.

2. Motility Limitation
    The inability to move an object or to do another task normally performed by using the musculoskeletal system.

3. Restricted Environment
    Bound to a place or status, or limited in activity, atmosphere, or progress.

4. Sensory Limitation
    The result of defect(s) in the transmission of information from the environment to the brain.

5. Communication Limitation
    A breakdown in the process by which information is exchanged between individuals through common symbols, signs, or behavior.

6. Pain Limitation
    When pain is continuing, unremitting, uncontrollable, and severe, it may constitute a severe functional limitation to normal living.

7. Debilitation or Exertional Limitation
    A condition in which the individual is in a weakened state for an extended time period.

8. Atypical Appearance
    Characteristics of an individual's physique and carriage that are inconsistent with what is considered acceptable by a culture.

9. Invisible Limitation
    Concealed or unapparent conditions that limit functions.

10. Substance Dependency
    Physical and/or psychological dependency.

11. Mental Limitation
    Developmentally Delayed (MR) and Learning Disabilities.

12. Consciousness Limitation
    Unconsciousness and other defects in consciousness.

13. Uncertain Prognosis
    Involves the stress and ambiguity of those medical conditions that have an unpredictable course of termination.

14. Dysfunctional Behavior
    Emotional disorders with deviant behavior. Also behavior due to cultural disadvantages.

A.   PSYCHOANALYSIS

1.   Chief figure is Sigmund Freud.

2.   Focus is on instinctual drives, unconscious motivation, and the past.

3.   Therapy is long-term, therapist is detached, and therapist is usually a psychiatrist.

4.   Terms

    a.   Transference – Client's distorted view of the relationship with the therapist based on past associations. (You're just like my father.)

    b.   Analysis of transference - Counselor encourages transference and then interprets the emotions.

    c.   Countertransference - Therapist foists (to pass off as genuine; to impose on another person) upon the client perceived relationships from past.

    d.   Id – Unconscious source of psychic energy ("pleasure seeker")

    e.   Ego - Mediates between the instincts and the surrounding environment ("balancer").

    f.   Superego - Moral code, inhibits Id impulses, strives for perfection (morals, morality)

    g.   Dream Analysis – "The royal road to the unconscious."

    h.   Free Association - Say whatever comes to mind.

    i.   Libido – Source of sexual energy, or sometimes thought to be source of general energy

5.   Defense Mechanisms

a.   Repression - A defense through which threatening or painful thoughts and feelings are excluded from awareness. An involuntary removal of something from consciousness (e.g. forgetting a childhood trauma).

b.   Reaction formation - In order to defend against a threatening impulse, actively express the opposite impulse (e.g.. being overly kind to someone you despise or renouncing homosexuality although you experience those feelings yourself).

c.   Denial - Closing one's eyes to the existence of threatening reality (e.g. refusing to accept that one has a drinking problem).

d.   Projection - Attributing to others one's own unacceptable desires and impulses (e.g. asking your partner if he is mad at you, when you are mad at him).

e.   Displacement - Directing hostility toward a "safe" object (e.g. being angry at the boss and therefore coming home and kicking the dog.).

f.   Rationalization - Manufacturing reasons for behavior, finding a "reason" for everything (e.g. claiming no remorse over the promotion you did not receive in order to conceal your disappointment).

g.   Sublimation - A redirection of sexual or aggressive energy into creative channels; this is the only healthy defense mechanism according to Freud (e.g. going jogging when you feel amorous and your partner is not available or boxing when feeling aggressive).

h.   Regression - Reverting to a form of outgrown behavior, an earlier phase of development in which demands were not so great (e.g. a teenager whose parents are contemplating divorce starts wetting the bed) .

i.   Ritual and undoing - Performing elaborate rituals as a way of undoing acts for which one feels guilty (e.g. the woman who cheats on her spouse comes home with a gift for her husband).

j. Compensation - Developing positive traits in order to make up for limitations (e.g. a person with total deafness becoming a master painter).

k. Identification - Enhancing self worth and compensating for one's sense of being a failure by identifying with people, organizations, or causes that are viewed as successful (e.g. a high school drop-out joining a gang).

l. Introjection - Taking in of other's values and standards (e.g. an abused child becoming an abuser).

6. Psychosexual Stages

Stage	Age	Fixation/Behavior
Oral	(0-1)	talkativeness, thumb sucking, smoking, biting
Anal	(1-3)	hoarding, neatness, guardedness, eating disorders
Phallic	(3-6)	non-resolution of own sexuality
Latency	(6-12)	NA
Genital	(12-18)	NA

B. ANALYTICAL PSYCHOLOGY OR JUNGIAN PSYCHOLOGY

1. Chief figure: Carl Gustav Jung.

2. Ego
    - Conscious mind - Sense of purpose & identity
    - Balances conscious & unconscious elements of psyche

    - Personal Unconscious
      Closely related to ego in that it may be unconscious but can be made conscious

4. Collective Unconscious
    - Psychic inheritance
    - Species knowledge
    - Never directly conscious of existence
    - Inferred through déjà vu, love at first sight, etc.
    - Can not be tested directly

5. Archetypes: The source of psychic energy
   - Psychological counterpart to instincts
   - Contents of Collective Unconscious
   - Examples, Mother, Child, Hero, Wise Old Man, Maiden, Animal (relations with humans)
   - Shadow - the dark side and the evil that we are *capable* of. Symbols include snakes, dragon, monsters and demons.
   - Persona - the public image (mask). The "good impression" or "false impression." "Sometimes we believe what we pretend to be."
   - Anima (female aspect in men e.g., represented by women in dreams) Can be good (fun loving) or bad (witch). Marriage can bring the two together.
   - Animus (male aspect in women in dreams).

6. The basis for the Myers-Briggs Type Indicator (see personality types below)

7. Personality types
   - **Introversion** (dreams, thoughts, feelings)
   - **Extroversion** (things, people, activities)
     (75% of population extroverted)
   - 4 Basic functions (not intended to be pathological - just differences)
     o Sensing (looking/listening) (75% of population)
     o Thinking (logically evaluating)
     o Intuiting (outside of usual conscious - eg. "Seeing around corners")
     o Feeling (evaluating the emotional responses)
     o Myers/Briggs added Judging (careful, inhibited)-Perceiving (more spontaneous)

C. ADLERIAN THERAPY

1. Chief figures are Alfred Adler and Don Dinkmeyer.

2. Focus on conscious aspects of behavior, and the importance of social forces in one's development and motivation.

3. Therapist provides encouragement, helps to change faulty motivation, endorses the development of social interest, and helps the client to identify his or her lifestyle.

4. Terms

    a. Lifestyle - Each person creates a lifestyle by age five primarily through interacting with other family members.

    b. Family Constellation - Emphasis on birth order.

    c. Early Recollections - One's perception of family atmosphere, rather than the events themselves, is crucial in the development of a lifestyle.

    d. Teleology - The belief that people are influenced by future goals as well as by past causes.

    e. Fictional finalism - Overgeneralization, e.g. believing that one will never get any breaks.

D. EXISTENTIAL THERAPY

1. Chief figures are Frankl, May, and Yalom.

2. Focus on importance of anxiety, freedom, choice, responsibility, and finding meaning in living.

3. Therapist facilitates a deep and personal relationship with client. Uses few techniques, and avoids psychological tests. The therapist confronts clients with the idea that they are responsible for their own lives.

4. Based on the belief that people form their lives by the choices that they make. When people realize that they have the freedom to make their own choices, this creates anxiety. This "normal" anxiety may be healthy and motivational, and lead to responsibility.

E.   PERSON CENTERED THERAPY

1.   Chief figure is Carl Rogers.

2.   Focus on the phenomenological world of the client and self actualization.

3.   Belief that the client has the capacity to solve his/her own problems - as long as the therapist provides unconditional positive regard, congruence, and empathy.

4.   Therapist utilizes active listening, reflection, and clarification.

5.   Terms

   a.   Phenomenology - The client's perception of reality is more important than the event itself.

   b.   Unconditional Positive Regard - Warmth, care, acceptance, and respect.

   c.   Congruence - Genuineness, giving up roles and facades.

   d.   Empathy - Ability of the counselor to feel with clients and convey this understanding back to them.

   e.   Self-Actualization - People have the basic tendency and striving to actualize, and to maintain and enhance their experiences.

F.   GESTALT THERAPY

1.   Chief figure is Fritz Perls.

2.   Gestalt = Wholeness. Stresses perception of completeness and wholeness. Helps individuals incorporate all parts of their lives, and resolve the past (unfinished business). Integration of all parts of the person.

3.   Focus on awareness of moment to moment experiencing and the belief that people are responsible for their own behavior and their active participation in feeling, sensing, seeing, and interpreting.

4.   In order to be in the here and now, a person must shed neurotic tendencies. The five layers of neuroses that interfere with one's being authentically in touch with oneself are:

    a.   The Phony - Pretending to be something one is not.

    b.   The Phobic - Avoiding recognizing aspects of self that one prefers to deny.

    c.   The Impasse - Wondering how one will make it in the environment.

    d. & e. The Implosive and the Explosive - Feeling vulnerable to feelings, but as the layers of defensiveness are peeled back, the person becomes alive in an explosion of joy, sorrow or pain that leads to becoming authentic. When a person reaches this point, the here and now can be fully experienced.

5.   Techniques

    a.   Dream Work - Clients present dreams and are directed to experience what it is like to be each part of the dream.

    b.   Empty Chair - Clients talk to various parts of their personality (i.e., dominant or passive side), and an empty chair is their focus.

    c.   Confrontation - Counselors point out to clients incongruent behaviors and feelings (i.e., client smiles when admitting to nervousness).

    d.   Making the Rounds - Used in a group when the counselor feels that a feeling expressed by one client should be faced by every member in the group.

    e.   I Take Responsibility - The client makes statements about perceptions, and ends the statement with the phrase "and I take responsibility for it."

    f.   Exaggeration - Exaggerating unwitting movement or gestures, in order to make the meaning of these behaviors more apparent.

G.   TRANSACTIONAL ANALYSIS

1.   Chief figure is Eric Berne.

2.   Focus on interaction, communication, early (in life) decisions, and the ability of each person to move beyond these early decisions.

3.   Structural Analysis - Belief that each person has three ego states: Parent, Adult, and Child. When people communicate with each other, each person chooses from one of the three ego states from which to draw their statements and responses. The three ego states are:

    a.   Parent - Do's, oughts, and shoulds.

        (1)   Nurturing Parent - Comforts and praises.

        (2)   Critical Parent - Finds fault, displays prejudices.

    b.   Adult - Objective thinking, data gathering.

    c.   Child - Childlike behavior and feelings.

        (1)   Natural Child - Spontaneous, impulsive, feeling oriented.

        (2)   Adaptive Child - Yields to wishes and demands of parental figures.

        (3)   Little Professor - Creative, intuitive.

While communicating, if persons are not operating from the same or complimentary ego states, then a "crossed transaction" occurs. This results in negative feelings.

4.   Terms

    a.   Strokes - Verbal or physical recognition. Negative strokes may be better than no strokes at all.

    b.   Injunctions - Negative messages.

    c.   Game – A set of transactions between people where at least one person loses. A series of strokes but alt least one person will feel bad. (E.g., Karpman Drama Triangle)

d.   Rackets- Unpleasant feelings following a game "I told you men are no good."

e.   Life scripts - Each person makes one by the age of five based on interpretations of external events. The ideal life script is "I'm OK, you're OK." People may operate from three other positions, however. These are "I'm OK, you're not OK," "I'm not OK, you're OK," and "I'm not OK, you're not OK."

H.   BEHAVIORISM

1.   Chief figures include Skinner, Bandura, Lazarus, and Wolpe.

2.   Based on the belief that all behavior is learned. Goals of therapy are to eliminate maladaptive behavior while learning adaptive behavior.

3.   Stresses current behavior and measurable treatment goals.

4.   Classical Conditioning links a stimulus with a response. Assumes that the organism is passive and reacting to the environment.

5.   Operant Conditioning takes place when the organism operates on the environment to its own advantage. Assumes that the organism is active, working toward a reward or punishment.

6.   Terms

a.   Positive reinforcement - Receiving something desirable as a consequence of a given behavior (e.g. getting a hug for cleaning up your room, adding something good).

b.   Negative reinforcement - Withdrawal or termination of an unpleasant stimulus as a result of performing a desired behavior (e.g. nagging ceases after the yard is raked; turning down heat at night so child will go to bed to be warm).

c.   Time out - Removing individual displaying undesired behavior (e.g. a child disruptive in the classroom is removed from the classroom).

d.   Overcorrection - The adolescent caught writing on her desk is told by the teacher to clean every desk in the classroom.

e. Response cost - A form of punishment in which a reinforcer is removed after an inappropriate or undesirable behavior occurs (e.g. in a token economy, it is when assignments are not completed that tokens are taken back by the instructor).

f. Feedback - Comments on the client's behavior after instructions (e.g. "Ken, I am pleased that you are on time for work today!").

g. Self reinforcement - Reinforcement given by self (e.g. after losing weight, going out and buying a new suit).

h. Self-management - A system in which people make decisions concerning specific behaviors they want to control or change themselves (e.g. a person interested in increasing assertiveness reads Your Perfect Right: A Guide To Assertive Behavior and devises a plan to become more assertive.)

i. Thought stopping - Inhibiting irrational or unwanted thoughts that interfere with concentration (e.g. replacing "Oh my God, I'm looking at the CRC and I know I'm going to fail and then never get my certification!" with "Question 1 is one I know. It says...").

j. Punishment - An adverse event that results from a person engaging in a given behavior (e.g. flunking a test as a result of not studying).

k. Modeling - Observational learning or imitating.

l. Shaping - Reinforcing any behavior that resembles the target behavior (e.g. in attempts to teach a child to make the bed, at first, the parent praises the child for simply pulling the covers up); incremental teaching

m. Extinction - Removing an unwanted behavior by failing to reinforce it (e.g. ignoring a child's temper tantrum); ignoring bad behavior

n. Continuous Reinforcement - Reinforcing the targeted behavior every time it occurs. Used to strengthen a given response (e.g. each time a child uses the toilet instead of the diaper, the parents clap and smile).

o. Intermittent Ratio Reinforcement - Reinforcing the target behavior after the response has occurred a set number of times. This is the best way to maintain a response (e.g. getting one full day off for a thirty day period without absenteeism).

p. Intermittent Variable Reinforcement - Reinforcing the target behavior after a set amount of time has passed, regardless of the number of times that the response has occurred. This may cause superstitious behavior (e.g. after winning once at the slot machine, the person continues to bet).

q. Systematic Desensitization - Designed to extinguish anxiety in particular situations. The client is taught to relax while at the same time describing situations that cause anxiety.

r. Assertiveness Training - Consists of counter-conditioning anxiety and reinforcing assertiveness. Usually includes modeling of desired behavior and client's role playing.

I. RATIONAL EMOTIVE BEHAVIOR THERAPY

1. Chief figure is Albert Ellis.

2. Goals of R.E.B.T. include helping people realize that they can live more rational and productive lives, assisting people in changing self-defeating thoughts and behaviors, and encouraging clients to be more tolerant of themselves and others.

3. Belief that thoughts influence feelings and behavior. If a person changes a way of thinking, then feelings and behaviors will be modified as a result.

    a. A - Activating event

    b. B - Belief about A

    c. C - Consequence (emotional reaction to B)

4. Focus on dispelling irrational beliefs through confrontation and re-education.

5. Therapist is active and direct, acting as a teacher, educating the client to the idea that events are without value until value is assigned to the event. The therapist is constantly confronting, disputing, and correcting the client's faulty beliefs.

6. R.E.B.T. is not recommended for clients who have mental impairments.

7. Techniques

   a. Cognitive Disputation - Direct questions, logical reasoning, and persuasion.

   b. Imaginal Disputation - Client imagines a stressful situation and examines his or her self-talk during that imagined situation.

   c. Behavioral Disputation - Client behaves in a way that is opposite of how he or she usually behaves. Includes bibliotherapy, homework, and role-playing.

J. REALITY THERAPY – CONTROL THEORY

1. Chief figures are William Glasser and Robert Wubbolding

2. Based on the premise that all behavior is directed toward basic human needs (e.g. belonging, being loved, feeling worthwhile). The therapist helps the client to formulate realistic plans to achieve personal needs and wishes.

3. Belief in the idea that humans create their own "failure identity" or "success identity" by the choices that they make. Responsible behavior leads to the formation of a success identity.

4. Control Theory - Behavior is under the control of perceptions (BCP). The brain acts as the control center, as it controls and regulates.

5. The therapist assists clients in evaluating what they are presently doing to see if it is working or not, accepting responsibility for their lives, and controlling their perceptions. The therapist does not accept excuses, opting instead for the natural consequences of irresponsible behavior. Does not emphasize childhood experiences.

6. Often used in prisons, schools, and youth detention centers

6.   The therapeutic relationship involves:

    a.   Making friends with the client.

    b.   Figuring out what client wants.

    c.   Evaluating whether or not current behavior is getting the client what he/she wants.

    d.   Determining what client wants to change.

    e.   Making plans for better choices.

    f.   Obtaining a commitment from client.

    g.   Not accepting excuses.

    h.   Natural consequences instead of punishment.

    i.   Never giving up on the client.

K.   Family Therapy

1.   Transgenerational Family Therapies

    a.   Chief Figure – Murray Bowen –

    b.   The core assumption of Bowen System Theory is that families and other natural systems respond in organized pattern behaviors.

    c.   A critical goal of Bowen Therapy is to help individuals differentiate from their family's emotional togetherness.

    d.   Bowen coaches his patients on how to "detriangle" from emotional family situations.

    e.   Review family structure through extended family members via genograms.

2.   Experiential Family Therapy

     a.   Chief figures – Virginia Satir; Carl Whittaker

     b.   Satir stressed the importance of congruent communication both between others and within self. If individuals are able to become more in touch with the messages within themselves, they are then able to communicate more congruently with others.

     c.   She also stressed the importance of fully experiencing emotion in families.

     d.   Techniques include family reconstructing, and role playing.

3.   Structural Family Therapy

     a.   Chief figure – Salvador Minuchin

     b.   Focus on structure of family systems.

     c.   Major concepts: Boundaries, family rules, "rubber fence" boundaries, hierarchy authority structure.

4.   Brief Family Therapy

     a.   Chief figures: Luige Boscolo, Gianfranco Cecchia

     b.   Strategic to solution focused.

     c.   Focus on solving problems using creative strategic interventions designed to bypass resistance.

     d.   Theory is more problem centered and pragmatic.

     e.   Focus on power games in family.

L.   Family Systems Theory general concepts (see above for individual descriptions)

     a.   Chief figures
- Alfred Adler (Adlerian family therapy)
- Murray Bowen (Multigenerational family therapy)
- Virginia Satir (Human validation process model)
- Carl Whitaker (Experiential/symbolic family therapy)
- Salvador Minuchin (Structural family therapy)

- Jay Haley and Cloe Madanes (Strategic Family therapy)
  Source: Corey, G. (2005). *Theories of Counseling and Psychotherapy.*
  Belmont, CA: Wadsworht/Brooks/Cole

b. Individuals are best understood within the context of relationships and through assessing the interactions within the entire family. Neither the individual nor the family are to "blame."

c. The client's problem may be a symptom of the family's dysfunction. "The problem may (1) serve a function or purpose for the family; (2) be a function of the family's inability to operate productively; or (3) be a symptom of dysfunctional patterns handed down across generations" (p. 387).

d. The client is connected to living systems and that change in one part affects all other parts.

e. Many therapists use genograms (family diagrams) to explore the family's process and rules. May include birth order and family birth dates, cultural and ethnic origins, religious affiliations, socioeconomic status, type of contact among family members, as well as proximity of family members.

M.   Feminist Counseling and Theory
       a. Chief Figures:
       - Marian Greenspan
       - Jean Baker Miller
       - Carolyn Zerbe Enns
       - Laura Brown
       - Olivia Espin

b. Basic Philosophies: Many traditional theories are based on power and gender-biased concepts and practices that conflict with women's psychological needs and development. Key constructs include gender free, interactionist, and life span orientation. The counseling relationship is egalitarian and women's experiences are honored. The relationship is also based on the empowerment of women which may lead to social change, legislative changes, and changing public policies.

c. Goal of Therapy: To assist client in reclaiming, recognizing, and using their personal power to free themselves from the limitations of a gender-role socialization. The approach can be applied to women and men with the goal of bringing about empowerment.

N. Narrative Therapy:
   a. Chief figures:
   - Michael White
   - David Epston.

    b. Basic Philosophies: Human nature is based on the idea that we have the ability to construct meaning in our lives and reauthor the meaning we attach to our lives. Each person's life is a story in progress. There is no such thing as a "fixed" sense of personhood. The narratives that we construct are selective.

    c.. Goal of therapy: The goal of therapy is to deconstruct dominant narratives and reauthor lives. The narrative counselor avoids being the expert in the counseling relationship.

O. Group Counseling

O.1 Corey and Corey (1997) identified four stages of group development. Stages include:

Stage 1-   Initial Stage - orientation and exploration

Stage 2-   Transition Stage - dealing with resistance

Stage 3-   Working Stage - cohesion and productivity

Stage 4-   Final Stage - consolidation and termination

O.2 The Therapeutic Factors In Group Therapy, Yalom's Curative Factors

1. Instillation of hope - If change is to occur, members must believe that change is possible.

2. Universality - Learning that others have some of the same bad thoughts and feelings.

3. Imparting of information - Didactic instructions about mental illness, mental health and general psychodynamics given by the group leader.

4. Altruism - Concern, consideration and affection for other people as opposed to self love or egoism.

5. The corrective recapitulation of the primary family group - One interacts with leaders and other members as one may have once interacted with parents and siblings.

6. Development of specializing techniques - The development of basic social skills.

7. Imitative behavior - Individuals may model themselves upon aspects of the other group members as well as the therapist.

8. Interpersonal learning - Understanding the importance of interpersonal relationships, corrective emotional experience and the group as a social microcosm.

9. Group cohesiveness - The attraction that members have for the group and for other members.

10. Catharsis - The expression of pent up feelings.

11. Existential factors - Learning that one must take ultimate responsibility for the way he/she lives their life no matter how much guidance and support is given by others.

Yalom, I.D. (1985). The Theory and Practice of Group Psychotherapy. 3rd Edition. Basic Books, Inc. New York.

O.3 Bruce Tuckman's small group process

1. Forming – Introductions and purpose of group established.

2. Storming – Conflicts, hidden agendas revealed, authority challenged, etc.

3. Norming – Group consensus emerges, purpose refined, and group strives to work together.

4. Performing – Members know how to work with one another.

5. Adjourning (added 1977)

Tuckman, B. W. (1965). Developmental sequences in small groups. Psychological Bulletin, 63, 384-399.
Tuckman, B. W., & Jensen, M. A. C. (1977). Stages of small group development revisited. Group and Organizational Studies, 2, 419- 427

PUBLIC SECTOR STATUS CODES

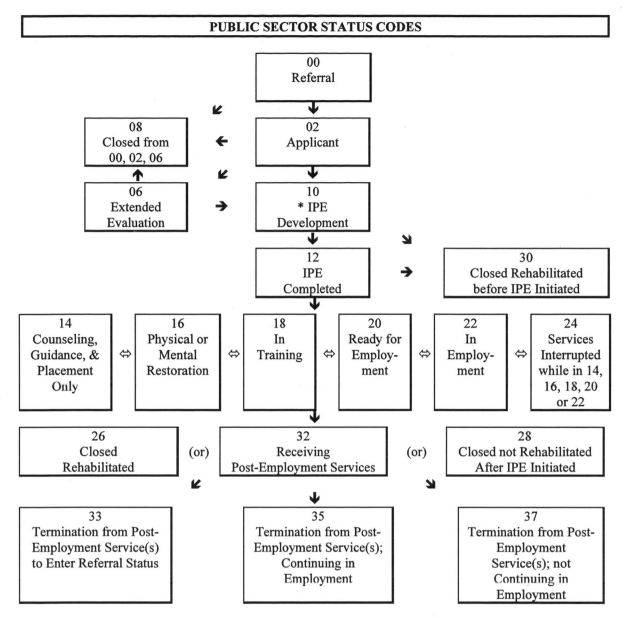

* IPE = Individual Plan for Employment

1. You have a 25-year-oldfemale client who has a T-6 complete spinal cord injury and she wants to become pregnant. You should:
    A) Discourage her from becoming pregnant because most paraplegic women miscarry during the first trimester.
    B) Explain to her that there is a 30% chance that her baby will be born with an incomplete closure of the spine, resulting in spina bifida.
    C) Educate her to the fact that most women with a spinal cord injury can give birth to a non-disabled baby.
    D) Discuss with her alternatives to childbirth such as adoption because her reproductive organs, which are below her level of injury, are no longer functioning to capacity.

2. You have a client who obtained a T-10 incomplete spinal cord injury due to an automobile accident that occurred while on the job as an emergency medical technician (EMT). Your client is now unable to perform many of the duties required of an EMT. The hospital he worked for, however, is willing to have him continue employment in some other capacity. You are currently exploring similar jobs that require the skills of an EMT. The best source to locate related titles to EMT and determine transferability of skills is the:
    A) Work Field code arrangement
    B) Dictionary of Occupational Titles
    C) Occupational Outlook Handbook
    D) Materials, Products, Subject Matter and Services

3. In the Classification of Jobs, requiring lifting of 50 pounds maximum with frequent and/or carrying of objects weighing up to 25 pounds is considered:
    A) Light Work
    B) Heavy Work
    C) Medium Work
    D) Very Heavy Work

4. You have a 32 year-old male client who has sustained a broken leg while working in his position as a truck driver. He is unable to do any work at his job. In Workers' Compensation terms, your client most likely has a:
    A) Temporary & Total Disability
    B) Temporary & Partial Disability
    C) Permanent & Total Disability
    D) Permanent & Partial Disability

5.   Your client tells you after taking a test she was found to be "social and enterprising."
     She can't remember the name of the test that she took that gave her this information.
     You suspect it's the
     A)   Sixteen PF
     B)   Valpar-17
     C)   MMPI
     D)   Strong Interest Inventory

6.   The Psychoanalytic Theory of Occupational Choice is based on the ego defense
     mechanisms of:
     A)   Justification and Identification
     B)   Compensation and Justification
     C)   Sublimation and Compensation
     D)   Sublimation and Identification

7.   Howard is your client and he has been diagnosed with Toruette's Syndrome. He is
     having trouble at work because
     A)   Recurring respiratory infections cause him to miss a lot of work.
     B)   His anemia is so severe he is often lethargic and stuporous.
     C)   His behavior is erratic and he often has outbursts of anger.
     D)   Due to his low IQ he is only able to work in a sheltered employment
          environment.

8.   Which of the following is an American National Standard Institute (ANSI) standard?
     A)   A ramp must be wide enough to contain one manual chair and should be wide
          enough to hold one power chair.
     B)   A ramp should be wide enough for two persons in power chairs to pass each
          other at one point on the route, and must be wide enough for one power or
          manual wheelchair along with one walking person.
     C)   A ramp must be wide enough for one wheelchair and one walking person, and
          should be wide enough for two wheelchairs to pass each other at one point on
          the route.
     D)   A ramp should be wide enough for a wheelchair and a walking person, and
          must be wide enough for at least one wheelchair.

9.   You have just received word that Reggie, a 30-year-old black male client of yours,
     has been approved for funding for full hip replacement surgery to be paid for by
     Public Sector Rehab. Reggie's diagnosis is:
     A)   Diabetes
     B)   Obsessive Compulsive Disorder
     C)   Sickle Cell Anemia
     D)   AIDS

10.   You are a member of a rehabilitation team, and the team has decided on a treatment plan for a particular client. You do not agree with the plan. You should:
A)   Still treat the client in the way you feel correct because to do otherwise is unethical.
B)   Follow the treatment plan as decided on by the team.
C)   Follow the treatment plan as decided on by the team, but explain to the client the way you think the plan should have been different.
D)   Explain to the client the team decision as well as your opinion, then let the client decide upon which treatment should be used.

11.   Satisfactoriness is a term central to:
A)   The Theory of Personality and Model Environments.
B)   The Theory of Early Parent-Child Relationships.
C)   The Minnesota Theory of Work Adjustment.
D)   The Need Drive Theory.

12.   Maria is diabetic and has trouble regulating her insulin. Independent of her Rehab Counselor she has found a job working in a grocery store. The opening is on the "graveyard " shift and she asks your professional advice concerning the suitability of the job considering her disability. You recommend that:
A)   She take it!
B)   She reconsider it.
C)   The job is okay if she can take her medication with her.
D)   The job is okay if she can take a 15 minute nap every 2 hours.

13.   Which one of the following does not use the Holland typology?
A)   Career Assessment Inventory
B)   Self-Directed Search
C)   Strong-Campbell Interest Inventory
D)   Minnesota Importance Questionnaire

14.   The difference between job satisfaction and job satisfactoriness is that:
A)   Job satisfaction represents how well an individual's abilities correspond with the ability requirements of the work environment whereas job satisfactoriness represents how well the work reinforces the individual.
B)   Job satisfaction represents how well the work reinforces the individual whereas job satisfactoriness represents how well an individual's abilities correspond with the ability requirements of the work environment.
C)   Job satisfaction represents how well an individual gets along with his boss whereas job satisfactoriness represents how long an individual remains in a particular work environment.
D)   Job satisfaction represents how well the work reinforces the individual whereas job satisfactoriness represents how long an individual remains in a particular work environment.

15. Calvin is your first client for Vocational Evaluation on Monday morning. He is impeccably dressed and cheery when the two of you meet. Before you open his file he asks where the bathroom is that he might wash his hands. He proudly reports it only took him three hours to dress for your appointment this morning and he owed all the credit to a behavior modification program he was enrolled in at a local hospital. Before you even open his file you expect Calvin has been diagnosed with
    A) Schizophrenia
    B) Conduct Disorder
    C) Major Depression
    D) Obsessive Compulsive Disorder

16. The member of the rehabilitation team who assists clients in developing skills that will be useful in performing activities of daily living is the:
    A) Psychiatrist
    B) Occupational Therapist
    C) Therapeutic Recreation Specialist
    D) Physical Therapist

17. Which of the following is an American National Standard?
    A) An accessible route (e.g. ramp) should not rise more than one foot for every twelve feet of length.
    B) An accessible route should not rise more than one foot for every 20 feet of length.
    C) An accessible route should not rise more than twelve feet for every 100 feet of length.
    D) An accessible route should not rise more than twelve feet for every 50 feet of length.

18. You have test results which have scores at the extreme. Which of the below is most affected by extremes?
    A) Mode
    B) Standard Deviation
    C) Mean
    D) Median

19. Rita is a 40-year-old client who reports to you, her Psychotherapist, that she still sucks her thumb at night. As a student of Freudian psychology you tell Rita her problem is that she is stuck in which stage?
    A) Oral
    B) Anal
    C) Genital
    D) Latency

20. Your client is a profoundly mentally retarded 15-year old female who never learned activities of self-grooming. Due to behavioral techniques that you have implemented in her treatment, she is now brushing her teeth and washing her face on a daily basis. Now that this response has been learned, the behavioral technique that you should use in order to maintain it is:
   A) Chaining
   B) Intermittent Reinforcement
   C) Direct Reinforcement
   D) Linking

21. Which scale represents DSM categories?
   A) Ordinal
   B) Nominal
   C) Predictive
   D) Ratio

22. Doris is your client and she has been seeking psychotherapy at her local Mental Health Center for the last six weeks. While in your office she uses words like "early decisions" and "inner child." You suspect that the therapy she has been receiving is based on the work of:
   A) Yalom
   B) Rogers
   C) Adler
   D) May
   E) Berne

23. Kelvin is dying of complications related to being HIV positive. He is a colleague and friend. During lunch one day he says that he is seeing a therapist who is helping him to live a "less restricted existence" and together they are searching for "meaning of life". You surmise that Kelvin is seeing a therapist who has studied the work of:
   A) Shalom
   B) Berne
   C) Adkins
   D) Frankl

24. The mean and standard deviation of the General Aptitude Test Battery are:
   A) 50 and 10
   B) 100 and 20
   C) 100 and 10
   D) 100 and 15

25.   The DuPont Study indicated that:
   A)   Federal legislation on affirmative action and nondiscrimination in employment practices has had a significant impact in encouraging employers to recruit, hire, and accommodate qualified minorities of all kinds, including persons with physical and mental impairments.
   B)   Employers are, by-in-large, uninformed about job accommodation and most particularly, how the process of planning and installing accommodations takes place.
   C)   Employees with disabilities are as productive as their non-disabled counterparts and even surpass their performance in areas such as attendance and safety.
   D)   Rehabilitation counselors employed by the State Division of Vocational Rehabilitation purchase work adjustment services from rehabilitation facilities significantly more often than rehabilitation counselors in the private sector.

26.   Which of the following disabilities has the lowest employment success rate?
   A)   Amputation of upper extremity
   B)   Acquired brain injury
   C)   Spinal cord injury
   D)   Diabetes

27.   Your client scored a 2 in the numerical subsection on the General Aptitude Test Battery. This means that your client scored in the:
   A)   top third of the population but not within the top 10%.
   B)   bottom third of the population but not within the bottom 10%.
   C)   middle third of the population.
   D)   top third of the population but not within the top 15%.

28.   The individual most associated with the a theory based on the belief that vocational development with women is different than men is:
   A)   Ann Roe
   B)   Carol Gilligan
   C)   Amanda Brill
   D)   Karen Horney

29.   You are interested in giving your client a test that yields immediate results. You choose the:
   A)   GATB
   B)   CAI
   C)   Apticom
   D)   16 PF

30. Which of the following interest inventories can be scored by the client?
    A) Career Assessment Inventory
    B) Strong-Campbell Interest Inventory
    C) Self-Directed Search
    D) Career Assessment Inventory - Enhanced Version

31. You have a 32-year-old male client who has one amputated leg. He has recently gone on a job interview and you are following up with the employer. The employer states that your client is probably capable of doing the work, but the employer is concerned about her worker's compensation insurance rates going up if she hires a person with a disability. You should:
    A) Explain to her that Worker's Compensation insurance rates are determined by the past safety record of the individual employees, and since your client's leg was amputated as a result of an infection rather than an injury, her safety record has not been effected by the amputation. Therefore, her rates will not increase as a direct result of hiring your client.
    B) Remind her that employers have a moral obligation to hire people who have disabilities.
    C) Review with her that the Worker's Compensation insurance rates increase only minimally as a result of hiring people who have disabilities.
    D) Explain to the employer that Worker's Compensation rates are determined by the business' risk factor and past safety record rather than the type of employees hired; therefore, her rates will not increase as a direct result of hiring your client.

32. You have a 21-year-old female client who has spina bifida. She has a high school diploma, and she recently completed training in a specific vocational area. Although she has gone on many job interviews over the past several weeks, employers are not hiring her to do work that she has been trained to do. Your client most likely has a (an):
    A) Occupational handicap
    B) Employment handicap
    C) Placement handicap
    D) B & C
    E) A & C

33. Your client, Jim, reports to you that he took a test several years ago in which he scored high on Mania and Hysteria. You believe he took the:
    A) Apticom
    B) Minnesota Multiphasic Personality Inventory
    C) Strong Interest Inventory
    D) Personality Differential Questionnaire

34. You have been requested to perform a job analysis. The best way to obtain the most accurate information about the job, you should:
    A) Interview several of the workers who perform the job-away from the job site in order to get the most objective information.
    B) Interview the employer extensively over the phone.
    C) Study the DOT definition and cross-reference in other appropriate arrangements and vocational books.
    D) Visit the job site and observe the work being done.

35. The criterion necessary for eligibility of state or federal rehabilitation programs are:
    A) Presence of a disabling condition; the condition constitutes a handicap to employment; there is a reasonable expectation that the employment handicap will last at least one year.
    B) Presence of functional limitation(s); constitutes a handicap to employment; client has been unemployed for at least one month since onset.
    C) Presence of a disabling condition; the condition constitutes a handicap to employment; there is a reasonable expectation that rehabilitation services will enable client to return to work.
    D) Presence of a disabling condition; the condition constitutes functional limitations; there is a reasonable expectation that the functional limitations will result in a handicap to employment.

36. According to the Minnesota Theory of Work Adjustment, the ultimate criterion of work adjustment is:
    A) Tenure
    B) Development of a vocational self-concept
    C) Satisfactoriness
    D) Satisfaction

37. Jose is your new client and throughout his evaluation you have suspected some problem with visual/motor coordination. You decide in addition to some psychological tests to give him a:
    A) Career Assessment Inventory
    B) Wide Range Achievement Test
    C) World Of Work Inventory
    D) Bender Gestalt

38. The negative effect on the performance of tasks or activities due to a medically defined condition is called a(n):
    A) Disability
    B) Handicap
    C) Functional limitation
    D) Impairment

39. A condition medically defined as a physiological, anatomical, mental, or emotional impairment is a:
   A) Disability
   B) Handicap
   C) Functional limitation
   D) Boo boo

40. The justification for public sector rehabilitation is that:
   A) Dependent clients are granted independent living services, thus reducing the need for costly institutional care and enabling clients to become productive members of society.
   B) A broad scope of clients are able to be served because private rehabilitation companies typically work only with catastrophic injuries.
   C) Many severely disabled clients are able to obtain vocational services because this population is often unable to afford private sector rehabilitation.
   D) Clients become taxpayers and thus rehabilitation services pay for themselves.

41. Regarding Social Security Disability Insurance and Supplemental Security Income, what is the primary factor that determines which benefit(s) a person with a disability may receive?
   A) Age
   B) Financial status
   C) Nature of the disability - Is it temporary or permanent?
   D) Employment status

42. You have a 29-year-old client who has had one of his limbs surgically removed as a result of severe electrical burns. His disability is referred to as:
   A) Triplegia
   B) Uniplegia
   C) Unidisarticulation
   D) Tridisarticulation

43. The ultimate effect(s) of a disability that derives directly from limitations imposed upon the individual, often by society, is termed a(n):
   A) Functional limitation
   B) Handicap
   C) Impairment

44. Working as a school counselor you hold up a picture in front of a 10 year old and ask him to tell a story about what is going on in the picture. You are administering a:
   A) Wide Range Achievement Test
   B) World of Work Inventory
   C) Personality Differential Questionnaire
   D) Thematic Apperception Test

45. The Job Club approach is primarily based on which counseling theory?
   A) Behaviorism
   B) Adlerian
   C) Existential
   D) Rogerian

46. In the General Aptitude Test Battery, "Q" is the abbreviation for:
   A) Motor Coordination
   B) Color Discrimination
   C) Eye-Hand-Foot Coordination
   D) Clerical Perception

47. Your client is a 20-year-old profoundly mentally retarded female who has been a productive client at a workshop for over one year. She recently obtained burns in an accident, and then became uncooperative with staff and peers in the workshop. She also began to refuse to work. As her rehabilitation counselor, you should:
   A) Refer her for psychotherapy
   B) Begin to research other facilities that she may feel more comfortable with and then make the new placement as soon as possible.
   C) Utilize time out in conjunction with negative reinforcement in order to extinguish her uncooperative and unproductive behavior.
   D) Focus on one small task that your client does enjoy at the workshop, reinforce her when she performs it and then build up from there.

48. Which test listed below is based on the works of Jung and is a well-known personality test
   A) Strong Interest Inventory
   B) Myers-Briggs
   C) Luria-Nebraska
   D) Minnesota Multiphasic Personality Inventory

49. The individual associated with the Occupational Theory of Early Parent-Child relationships is:
   A) Roe
   B) Ginsberg
   C) Super
   D) Hoppock

50. According to the Social Security Administration, how long must a person's disability be expected to last in order for the person to be qualified for SSDI?
   A) Six months
   B) One year
   C) 18 months
   D) Two years

51. The individual who claimed that selecting an occupation is a compromise because many possible decisions are thus eliminated is:
    A) Super
    B) Roe
    C) Ginzberg
    D) Hoppock

52. While reading a VDARE you notice the client in the report has a high rating in "V". This implies an aptitude in which area?
    A) Visual-Motor
    B) Verbal
    C) Visual
    D) Spatial

53. A Physiatrist is a:
    A) Physical therapist also trained in physical medicine.
    B) A rehabilitation nurse qualified to also do physical therapy.
    C) A medical doctor specializing in physical medicine and rehabilitation.
    D) A medical doctor with additional training in psychiatric services.

54. The study that found workers with disabilities to have equal or greater productivity rates than non-disabled workers was titled the:
    A) Hawthorne Study
    B) Reeces Study
    C) Berkley Study
    D) DuPont Study

55. Which of the following is true about Supported Employment?
    A) Supported employment is a method of rehabilitation intervention in which a professional staff person, known as a job coach, provides structured job placement services and highly individualized and intensive training at the job site.
    B) In the supported-employment model, the amount and type of intervention is based on the interests of the client.
    C) Supported employment began in the late 1970's through university-based demonstration programs, and it is currently being expanded through federal legislation so that it will become an integral part of the federal-state vocational rehabilitation system by 1995.
    D) Most supported employment programs have primarily served persons with profound learning disabilities.

56. The vocational evaluation report you are reading suggests that the client's lifting be limited to 10 lbs. This information concurs with the medical report contained in the client's file. The client should be placed in a job that is:
    A) Light
    B) Sedentary
    C) Medium
    D) None of the above

57. The ultimate goal of systematic desensitization is to:
    A) Teach coping skills
    B) Extinguish targeted anxiety
    C) Decrease overt pain behavior
    D) Extinguish overt pain behavior

58. The best predictor of outcome of rehabilitation for a traumatic brain injured client is:
    A) The post-injury IQ
    B) The location of the injury within the brain
    C) The length of the coma
    D) Family support

59. Which one of the following is <u>not</u> a scale on the Minnesota Multiphasic Personality Inventory?
    A) Homosexuality
    B) Depression
    C) Hysteria
    D) Psychopathic Deviant

60. The individual most associated with the theory that individuals develop and implement a self-concept within the occupational world by going through basic stages is:
    A) Super
    B) Ginzberg
    C) Holland
    D) Hershenson

61. Raymond was recently blinded in an industrial accident and has been referred to you for vocational counseling. You decide the Haptic is just too arduous to administer and decide to use a subtest of the:
    A) Wechsler Adult Intelligence Scale
    B) Stanford-Binet Scales
    C) Wide Range Achievement Test
    D) Bender Gestalt Visual Motor Test

62. You are reading a VDARE prepared by a rehabilitation counselor and you notice "K" in the aptitudes section. You know this is a reference to the client's aptitudes in what area?
    A) Motor coordination
    B) Visual
    C) Clerical
    D) Hearing

63. In the DSM-IV, mental retardation would be listed as what Axis?
    A) Axis I
    B) Axis II
    C) Axis III
    D) Axis IV

64. The most frequently used measure for the evaluation and diagnosis of clinical personality symptoms and disorders is the:
    A) 16 Personality Factor Questionnaire
    B) Rorschach
    C) Minnesota Multiphasic Personality Inventory
    D) Minnesota Importance Questionnaire

65. How is the Job Club method different from other job-seeking techniques?
    A) It includes video recording equipment for role playing, modeling, and simulation exercises.
    B) It includes vocational evaluation.
    C) It includes remedial training.
    D) It includes peer reinforcement.

66. Your client has symptoms of causalgia. She most likely has:
    A) A personality disorder
    B) A lot of pain
    C) First degree burn
    D) Quadriplegia/Tetraplegia

67. The family doctor suggests that the patient see a specialist because symptoms of MS are evident. The specialist most likely recommended is a (an):
    A) Neurologist
    B) Oncologist
    C) Cardiologist
    D) Orthopedic surgeon

68. The theorist who claimed that occupational choice is a progressively irreversible process is:
    A) Tiedman
    B) Hoppock
    C) Ginzberg
    D) Allport

69. After discovering that your child has a seizure disorder, the principal of her school refuses to develop an educational plan that is individualized for her educational needs. You insist that the school comply with the law. The law you are referring to is:
    A) P.L. 93-112
    B) P.L. 95-602
    C) P.L. 90-391
    D) I.D.E.A.

70. The highest job that the Social Security Administration defines as "unskilled" is a job that requires:
    A) A short demonstration only
    B) Up to thirty days training
    C) Up to three months of training
    D) Over three months and up to six months of training

71. You have been working with a Job Club in which most members are quadriplegics and high paraplegics. You recommend that they tell potential employers what their needs are in the workplace. The most important thing in the list below is:
    A) Moderate temperature
    B) An accessible area with a couch where one can lie down during the day for short naps
    C) Having a quiet work area with few distractions
    D) No vibrations

72. This person pioneered a system of seeking employment called Job Club.
    A) Bandura
    B) Welder
    C) Maslow
    D) Azrin

73. Which theorist is most closely associated with "Family Systems"?
    A) Bowen
    B) Satir
    C) Minuchin
    D) Boscolo

74. You are working at an emergency mental health receiving facility and a man comes in stating that he doesn't know where he is, what is happening to him or who he is. He is brought in by a police officer who picked him up because he was wandering around in the streets shouting at cars that passed by. In your initial assessment of this man you describe him as:
    A) Neurotic
    B) Disassociative
    C) Psychotic
    D) Over-medicated

75. Tom has recently returned to work after back surgery. His employer hires him knowing of his injury at his last job and places him in a less physically demanding job. His job is classified as sedentary. While performing his job his back becomes aggravated and his doctor recommends more treatment. Tom's boss is concerned about the rise in health care costs to the other employees and:
    A) Contacts the Second Injury Fund in their state.
    B) Contacts the company lawyer and files a suit against Tom.
    C) Tells Tom he will be fired and the company will not pay for any health care.
    D) because the injury existed previous to his employment.

76. The identifying characteristic of a person with Cystic Fibrosis is their inability to
    A) Break down food and store it as fat
    B) Walk
    C) Expel mucus
    D) Control their intake of sugar

77. Dedicated to ensuring the rights of persons with disabilities, this woman is considered one of rehabilitation's earliest leaders. She is:
    A) Nightingale
    B) Donaldson
    C) Withers
    D) Switzer

78. This educator expanded opportunities for persons with visual impairments.
    A) Dix
    B) Howe
    C) Rogers
    D) Gallaudet

79. If post employment services in public sector rehabilitation are planned by the time the IPE is written, should these services be included in the plan ?
    A) No.
    B) Yes.
    C) Only with people with "severe" disabilities.
    D) Only if the plan is expected to be completed in one year or less.

80. Your client is a twenty-year-old male with MR that resulted from trauma at birth. He lives with his parents and is working with a state rehabilitation counselor who has drawn up his IPE. The client's IQ is 55. Will his parents be expected to sign his IPE?
    A) No.
    B) Yes.
    C) Only if he agrees.
    D) What's an IPE?

81. Often State Rehabilitation Evaluators confer with field counselors about their experience with the client during testing and what results the tests yielded. They are able to do this because of
    A) Confidentiality
    B) Appropriate Disclosure
    C) Because they work for the State
    D) Need to know and the field counselor made the referral

82. The level of education, aptitude and vocational functioning a person has following an injury is abbreviated by on the VDARE (transferability worksheet) as:
    A) AMA
    B) CAC
    C) RFC
    D) PVF

83. When consulting the GOE a user can expect the job titles to be arranged by:
    A) Titles
    B) Products
    C) Interest factors
    D) Aptitudes

84. When consulting the Industrial Designation code one should expect jobs to be arranged according to:
    A) Titles
    B) Products
    C) Interest factors
    D) Aptitudes

85.   The D.O.T. is published by the:
        A)   The Dept. of the Navy
        B)   The Census Bureau
        C)   The Dept. of Labor
        D)   Bureau of Labor Statistics

86.   Work that requires 100 or more pounds of lifting is referred to as:
        A)   Strenuous
        B)   Medium
        C)   Heavy
        D)   Very Heavy

87.   Work that requires a maximum of 20 pounds of lifting is described as:
        A)   Medium
        B)   Light
        C)   Very Light
        D)   Sedentary

88.   General Education Development is scored on a scale of:
        A)   1-6
        B)   1-9
        C)   1-10
        D)   1-100

89.   Which of the following provides pre-screening to employers?
        A)   Job development
        B)   Job placement
        C)   Job satisfaction
        D)   Job accommodation

90.   One of the purposes of Workers' Compensation law is to:
        A)   Encourage safety in the workplace.
        B)   Reduce the cost of health insurance.
        C)   Help attorneys make a living.
        D)   Pay the vocational costs for most injured workers.

91.   The amount of Workers Compensation received by an injured employee is usually what per cent (up to a maximum) of the former pay?
        A)   50
        B)   75
        C)   100
        D)   66

92. In worker's compensation, an open head injury is an example of which of the following?
   A) Unscheduled injury
   B) Scheduled injury
   C) Partial injury
   D) Permanent and total injury

93. In a sheltered workshop the primary emphasis is on:
   A) Vocational readjustment and reentry into the competitive labor market.
   B) Placing a person in a protected work environment when they are not able to work at a "competitive" level.
   C) Making sure the client receives at least minimum wage.
   D) Meeting the requirements of the various contracts for work.

94. In the absence of an occupational handicap, a person with a disability may have difficulty securing work due to an employment handicap such as:
   A) Work Tolerance
   B) Atypical Appearance
   C) Discrimination
   D) Pain

95. The ability to <u>find</u> employment is:
   A) Placeability
   B) Employability
   C) Job Readiness
   D) Labor Force Participation Rate

96. I am a M.D. specializing in obesity. What am I?
   A) Bariatrist
   B) Internist
   C) Physiologist
   D) Pysiatrist

97. I create artificial limbs for persons requiring them. What am I?
   A) Orthotist
   B) Physical Therapist
   C) Prosthetist

98. I tailor exercise and range of motion programs to my individual clients. My goal is to increase strength, reduce pain and restore a person physically. I am a:
   A) Physical Therapist
   B) Exercise Neurologist
   C) Strength Trainer
   D) Chiropractor

99. What should a rehabilitation counselor watch out for when forming a job club?
    A) "Stagnation" caused by participants' lack of motivation.
    B) The business community perceiving the Job Club as being business oriented rather than as a treatment or service agency.
    C) Participants hoarding job leads.
    D) Staff lacking expertise in job coaching.

100. What is the purpose of the initial interview in a rehabilitation counseling setting?
    A) To determine client need for rehabilitation services.
    B) To establish the relationship.
    C) To determine eligibility for services.
    D) To assess client motivation to pursue vocational goals.

101. Workers' Compensation rates are determined by which of the following?
    A) The number of disabled people employed by the company and the average amount of work-related injuries taking place in that field.
    B) The number of disabled people employed by the business.
    C) Past accident rate and amount charged to its insurance carrier.
    D) Past accident rate and amount charged to the employer.

102. The leading cause of death among persons with Spinal Cord Injury is:
    A) Nonischemic Heart Disease
    B) Respiratory Disease
    C) Renal Failure
    D) Malignant Decubiti

103. Your client with Cystic Fibrosis is job hunting. Vocational concerns include?
    A) Avoid heights due to vertigo.
    B) Avoid fumes and particles in the air due to respiratory problems.
    C) Avoid dangerous machinery due to visual deficits.
    D) Avoid irregular work hours due to the need to regulate blood sugar.

104. What publication would have detailed information on Dysthymia?
    A) Physician's Desk Reference
    B) Standards on Neurological Classification
    C) Diagnostic and Statistical Manual (DSM)
    D) Journal of Disability Policy Studies

105. Your client has been diagnosed as chronically depressed. Which of the following is an operational behavior you might observe?
    A) Showing up late for work.
    B) Hallucinating.
    C) Experiencing dizziness due to temperature changes.
    D) Acting depressed while on the job.

106. Your client has a C-6 complete spinal cord injury. Which of the following vocational considerations is most important to recommend?
    A) Avoid working near dangerous machinery due to problems with balance.
    B) Avoid jobs requiring repetitive motion of the upper limbs due to the likelihood of spasms.
    C) Avoid jobs likely to reinforce pain behavior.
    D) Avoid jobs involving extremes of heat or cold due to the body's inability to regulate temperature.

107. Your client has ankylosing spondylitis. Which of the following would you recommend regarding vocational considerations?
    A) Look for a sedentary job that allows for frequent changes in position.
    B) Look for a job that takes place indoors, as outside work is likely to take place on uneven ground.
    C) Direct your client to jobs requiring bending and twisting, as these movements are considered therapeutic and pain-relieving.
    D) Steer your client away from noisy environments, as the vibrations contribute to and worsen the headaches.

108. Which of the following is typical in someone with a histrionic personality?
    A) Violent motor activity
    B) Irrational fear
    C) Delusions of grandeur
    D) Overly silly and giggly

109. The behavioral technique of extinction would be most likely used to treat the excessive target behavior of:
    A) Acting out
    B) Depression
    C) Temper Tantrums
    D) Passive-Aggressive behavior

110. What is the difference between SSI and SSDI?
    A) SSI is private disability insurance and SSDI is public disability insurance.
    B) SSI and SSDI have different "means" tests.
    C) SSI is insurance and SSDI is for welfare recipients
    D) SSI is only available to people who have a work history.

111. You are reading the medical records of a new client. It is written that the client is bipolar. You know that this is a:
    A) Mood disorder
    B) Personality disorder
    C) Psychosis
    D) Neurosis

112. Which of the following best reflects the difference between a situational assessment and a job analysis?
    A) A situational assessment measures specific parts of a job, while a job analysis is used to assess the job as a whole.
    B) A situational assessment is used to analyze worker abilities, while job analysis is used to assess job requirements.
    C) A situational assessment is used to assess the requirements of one specific job, while a job analysis is used to arrange jobs by similarity in a field.
    D) A situational assessment is used to assess job requirements, while a job analysis is used to assess worker requirements.

113. Which of the following is true regarding multiple sclerosis?
    A) It is predictable but unstable.
    B) It is predictable and stable.
    C) It is unpredictable and unstable.
    D) It is unpredictable and stable.

114. Peripheral neuropathy is likely to be found secondary to:
    A) Diabetes
    B) Pulmonary dysfunction
    C) Obesity
    D) Neuromuscular disease

115. You have an 18-year-old client with a T-5 (complete) spinal cord injury who was just accepted to the local university. Because accessibility is an issue, you advise your client to find out ahead of time where his classes are located. He calls you one week later and states that his Algebra class is planning to meet on the second floor of a building with no elevator. Which of the following would you do?
    A) Request that the school provide a tutor for your client at no extra cost to provide private instruction.
    B) Demand that the school remove all barriers in the building so that your client can attend the class with his classmates.
    C) Work with a guidance counselor in identifying another section of the Algebra class that takes place in an accessible location.
    D) Request that the school move the Algebra class to an accessible location.

116. The Merck Manual is used to:
    A)   Determine the percentage of body burned.
    B)   Look up information on jobs that are arranged by work activity or product.
    C)   Look up information on physical diseases.
    D)   Determine a client's eligibility for Supplemental Security Income and Social Security Disability Insurance.

117. You have a 25-year-old client with epilepsy who has applied for a job as store clerk. The owner of the store expresses concern to you because this job position occasionally requires driving for deliveries. Your client is on seizure medication but has a good driving records. What would you do?
    A)   Point out to the employer that driving for deliveries is rarely needed and that it is not on the job description; therefore, another employee should be able to do it.
    B)   Tell the employer that a medical board can review your client's driver's license if your client first receives a conditional job offer.
    C)   Tell the employer that your client will take the responsibility of locating a family member to assist with driving when needed.
    D)   Explain to the employer that although your client has epilepsy, he was able to get a drivers' license because he went accident-free with a one-year probationary learner's permit.

118. You have a new client and during your initial meeting with her she reports "I used to be an athlete, but four months ago I had a spinal cord injury. The doctors told me it's a T-3 incomplete injury." You suspect that the best predictor for her adjustment is:
    A)   Whether or not she will be able to excel in adapted sports.
    B)   The meaning of disability for her.
    C)   The extent of her family and friends' support.
    D)   Whether she will use a wheelchair or crutches with braces.

119. An IQ of 48 would classify a person as:
    A)   mildly mentally retarded
    B)   moderately mentally retarded
    C)   severely mentally retarded
    D)   profoundly mentally retarded

120. You have a client with arthritis, and you plan to evaluate her manual dexterity. Which of the following assessment tools would you select?
    A)   Differential Aptitude Test
    B)   Purdue Pegboard
    C)   Barthel Inventory
    D)   Leiter Index

1. C	31. D	61. A	91. D
2. A	32. D	62. A	92. A
3. C	33. B	63. B	93. B
4. A	34. D	64. C	94. C
5. D	35. C	65. D	95. A
6. D	36. A	66. B	96. A
7. C	37. D	67. A	97. C
8. D	38. C	68. C	98. A
9. C	39. A	69. D	99. C
10. B	40. D	70. B	100. B
11. C	41. B	71. A	101. C
12. B	42. C	72. D	102. B
13. D	43. B	73. B	103. B
14. B	44. D	74. C	104. C
15. D	45. A	75. A	105. A
16. B	46. D	76. C	106. D
17. A	47. D	77. D	107. A
18. C	48. B	78. B	108. D
19. A	49. A	79. B	109. C
20. B	50. B	80. A	110. B
21. B	51. C	81. D	111. A
22. E	52. B	82. C	112. B
23. D	53. C	83. C	113. C
24. B	54. D	84. B	114. A
25. C	55. A	85. C	115. D
26. B	56. B	86. D	116. C
27. A	57. B	87. B	117. A
28. B	58. C	88. A	118. C
29. C	59. A	89. A	119. B
30. C	60. A	90. A	120. B

Appendix 4
CRC TEST TAKING CHECKLIST

	Become familiar with layout of test.
	READ the directions!!
	Do NOT scan questions. Read the entire question.
	Allot time wisely - pace yourself. Bring a watch with you.
	Skip the difficult questions and come back to them later.
	Do not become upset if you are unable to answer a question.
	Answer the questions that are asked, i.e. read and understand the question!
	Read every answer. Usually can discard all but two answers.
	Do not change answers unless you are **certain**.
	Usually avoid "all", "every time", "always" answers.
	Make sure the answer on the separate answer sheet corresponds with the question number.
	There is no penalty for guessing.
	Obtain adequate sleep.
	Dress for coolness.
	Do NOT eat a LARGE breakfast or lunch.
	Avoid mind dulling drugs/foods several days prior to exam (e.g. alcohol).
	Be confident! Have a positive attitude! Most people pass!

Appendix 5
CRC EXAM GUIDE EVALUATION

On a scale of 1 to 5 please evaluate this study guide.

1.   How well was the study guide organized?

1	2	3	4	5
Poor	Fair	Good	Very Good	Excellent

Comments:

2.   How well did the study guide cover the subject?

1	2	3	4	5
Poor	Fair	Good	Very Good	Excellent

Comments:

3.   How easy was the study guide to read?

1	2	3	4	5
Poor	Fair	Good	Very Good	Excellent

Comments:

4.   How well did the study guide help prepare you for the exam?

1	2	3	4	5
Poor	Fair	Good	Very Good	Excellent

Comments:

5.   What changes, additions, etc. should we make? Add any comments you wish.

Immediately After The Exam Please return to:
Dr. Roger Weed
Counseling and Psychological Services
Georgia State University
P. O. Box 3980
Atlanta GA 30302-3980

Or email comments to rweed@gsu.edu

APPENDIX 6
REFERENCES

Andrew, J. & Faubion, C. (Eds.) (2002). *Rehabilitation Services: An introduction for the human services professional*. Osage Beach, MO: Aspen.

Bolton, B. (1987). *Handbook of measurement and evaluation in rehabilitation*. Baltimore: Paul H. Brooks.

Brodwin, M., Tellez, F. & Brodwin, S. (Eds.). (2002). *Medical, psychosocial and aspects of disability*. Athens, Ga: Elliott & Fitzpatrick.

Bryan, W. V. (1999). *Multicultural aspects of disabilities: A guide to understanding and assisting minorities in the rehabilitation process*. Springfield, Illinois: Charles C. Thomas Publisher, LTD.

Corey, G. (2005). *Theory and practice of counseling and psychotherapy*. Monterey, CA: Brooks/Cole.

Corey, G. & Corey, S (1997). *Group counseling theory and practice*. Monterey, CA: Brooks/Cole.

William Daubert, et ux., etc., et al., Petitioners v. Merrell Dow Pharmaceuticals, Inc. June 28, 1993 U. S. Supreme Court # 92–102.

Field, T. & Field J. (2004). *Classification of jobs*. Athens, Ga: Elliott and Fitzpatrick.

Field, T. & Weed, R. (1988). *Transferable work skills*. Athens, Ga: Elliott and Fitzpatrick.

Giles, F. L. (1992). *The vocational rehabilitation of minorities*. (ERIC Document Reproduction Service No. ED358592).

Kapes, B. (1988). A counselor's guide to career assessment instruments. National Career Development Assoc.

Kumho Tire v Patrick Carmichael March 23, 1999, U.S. Supreme Court # 97-1709.

Marshall, C. (ed). (2001). *Rehabilitation and American Indians with disabilities*. Athens, GA: Elliott & Fitzpatrick.

Rubin, S. E. & Roessler, R. T. (1995). *Foundations of the vocational rehabilitation process* (4th ed.). Austin, TX: Pro-ed.

Sue, D. W. & Sue, D. (1999). *Counseling the culturally different: Theory and practice* (3rd ed.). New York: John Wiley & Sons, Inc.

Stolov, W. & Clowers, M. (Eds.). (1981). *Handbook of severe disability.* Washington, D.C.: Rehabilitation Services Administration, Department of Education.

Shrey, D. & Lacerte, M. (1995). *Principles and Practices of Disability Management in Industry.* Boca Raton: CRC Press.

USDOL (1991). *Dictionary of occupational titles, 4th ed.* Washington, DC: U.S. Government Printing Office.

Weed, R. & Field, T. (2001). *Rehabilitation consultant's handbook (3rd ed.).* Athens, Ga: Elliott & Fitzpatrick Vocational Services.

Weed. R (Ed.) (2004). *Life Care Planning and Case Management Handbook* (2nd ed.). Boca Raton, FL: St. Lucie/CRC Press.

Wright, G. (1980). *Total rehabilitation.* Boston: Little, Brown and Co.

ABOUT THE AUTHORS

Roger O. Weed, Ph.D., CRC, CDMS, CCM, LPC, FIALCP, FNRCA, is the graduate rehabilitation counseling coordinator and professor at Georgia State University in the Department of Counseling and Psychological Services. He has authored or co-authored more than 150 books, chapters, and articles relating to rehabilitation. He is also Fellow of the National Rehabilitation Counseling Association and Fellow of the International Academy of Lie Care Planners.

Joseph A. Hill, Ph.D., CRC, is a member of the clinical faculty in the Department of Counseling and Psychological Services at Georgia State University. He is training director for the counseling psychology program and coordinates the doctoral internships. He also holds adjunct faculty status with the Georgia State University Counseling Center. He is a certified rehabilitation counselor, licensed psychologist, and a licensed professional counselor.

191